INSPIRE COMPUTING

International

Workbook ⎯ YEAR **8**

Paul Clowrey

Pearson

Detailed contents

Welcome to Inspire Computing!

Whether for school, fun, work or staying in touch with relatives around the world digital technology is all around us.

Through coverage of ICT and Computer Science you will discover how this amazing technology works, how it connects the world together and it has revolutionised the classroom, workplace, and home.

Learning objectives
This is what you will know or be able to do by the end of the lesson.

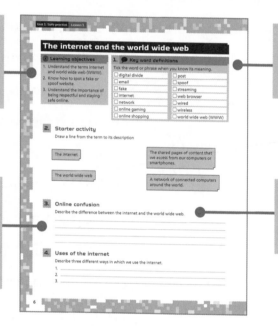

Key words definitions
Test your knowledge of the key word

Activity
You might need to write or draw an answer, circle pictures or words, or tick or match answers.

Instruction
Read this carefully to know what to do.

8. Plenary quick quiz

Plenary quick quiz
A fun way to test what has been understood from the lesson.

Question 1	Question 2	Question 3	Question 4	Question 5
True or false? Only online videos can be embedded in a slide.	Name the device required to record sound.	What is the movement from one slide to another called?	True or false? If the website changes, any embedded content will disappear.	Which of the following is not a form of interactivity?
☐ true ☐ false	☐ speaker ☐ projector ☐ mouse ☐ microphone	☐ text box ☐ transition ☐ animation ☐ sound effect	☐ true ☐ false	☐ navigation ☐ website links ☐ use of logos ☐ sound clips

We hope you will find this book useful in developing your knowledge of digital technology, its effective use of applications and in supporting future learning.

Each topic includes easy to understand theory, real-world examples, and ideas for further investigation. You can also test your knowledge of keywords and regular exam-quality questions with supported answers. A checkpoint at the end of each lesson is a quick and easy way to check your own understanding.

Short answer questions
Questions to solidify your learning and prepare you for your exam.

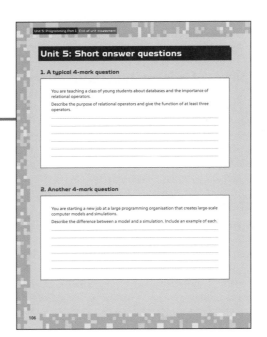

Revision checklist
Ensuring you are covering all revision forms for your learning and finding what works best for you!

Vector graphics

◎ Learning objectives

1. Understand the nature and purpose of a vector image.
2. Understand how a vector image can be created using coordinates.
3. Know how and why vectors are used for specific situations.

1. 💬 Key word definitions

Tick the word or phrase when you know its meaning.

☐ coordinate   ☐ scale down

☐ geometry   ☐ scale up

☐ image quality   ☐ vector

2. Starter activity

Give three pieces of information required to create a vector.

1. ....

2. ....

3. ....

3. Benefits of vectors

Describe three benefits of vector graphics.

1. ....

2. ....

3. ....

4. Real-world uses of vectors

Describe two real-world uses of vectors.

1. ....

   ....

2. ....

   ....

5. Create a vector

Create a vector using the instructions below:

Graphic 1:

Start: X4, Y2

End: X9,Y8

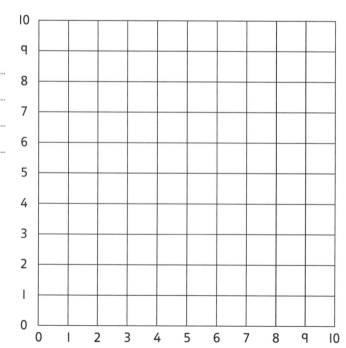

6. Vector instructions

Complete the missing instructions for the graphic shown:

Graphic 1:

Start: X3, Y3

Mid: X5, Y10

End: ....

Fill colour: ....

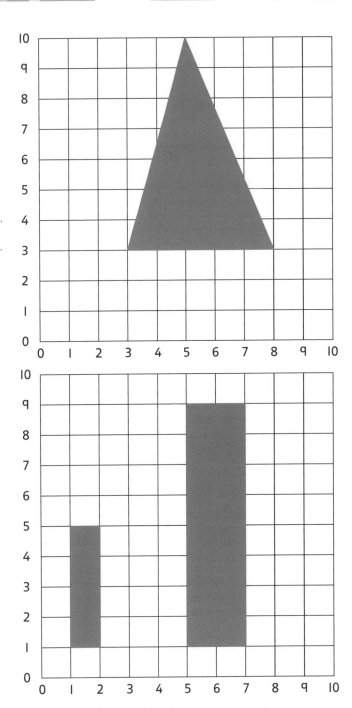

7. Vector scaling

What scale has been used to create the graphic on the right from the graphic on the left?

....

8. Plenary quick quiz

Question 1	Question 2	Question 3	Question 4	Question 5
Which of the following is similar to a vector graphic?	True or false? Vectors lose quality when increased in size.	Which of the following is not required to create a vector?	What is used to halve a vector graphic of a rectangle?	X3, Y4 to X6, Y9 are examples of?
☐ bitmap	☐ true	☐ start point	☐ scaling	☐ pixels
☐ dot to dot	☐ false	☐ end point	☐ resolving	☐ algorithms
☐ a photo		☐ line type	☐ pixelating	☐ coordinates
☐ a sketch		☐ resolution	☐ reversing	☐ 3D shapes

Creating a vector graphic

◎ Learning objectives

1. Understand how a graphic can be created using multiple points.
2. Demonstrate understanding of how to create a simple recognisable vector graphic.

1. 💬 Key word definitions

Tick the word or phrase when you know its meaning.

☐ algorithm   ☐ vector

☐ image quality

2. Starter activity

Describe how an algorithm can be used to create a vector graphic.

....

....

3. Simple graphic

Create a simple graphic using the following instructions:

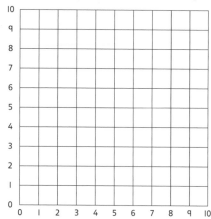

Shape 1:
X1,Y1   X1,Y9   X9,Y9   X9,Y1

Shape 2:
X5, Y5, R3

4. Missing coordinates

Complete the missing coordinates to create the graphic below.

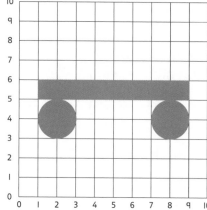

Shape 1:
X2, Y4, R1

Shape 2:
X_,Y_   X_,Y_   X_,Y_   X_,Y_

Shape 3:
X8, Y4, R1

5. Character vector art

Create a character graphic using the following instructions.

Shape 1:
X2, Y8, R1

Shape 2:
X8, Y8, R1

Shape 3:
X5, Y5, R4

Shape 4:
X4, Y6, R1

Shape 5:
X4, Y6, R0.5

Shape 6:
X6, Y6, R1

Shape 7:
X6, Y6, R0.5

Shape 8:
X5, Y5, R0.5

Line 1:
X5, Y4 X5, Y3

Line 2:
X4, Y2, X5, Y3

Line 3:
X5, Y3, X6, Y2

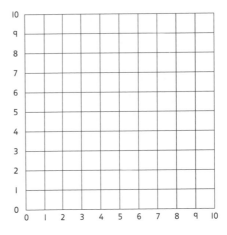

6. Plenary quick quiz

Question 1	Question 2	Question 3	Question 4	Question 5
What does the R in vector instructions stand for?	What is a programming app that can create simple graphics called?	True or false? The horizontal axis is labelled as Y.	When defining a circle, what do the X and Y coordinates refer to?	Name the device that uses coordinates to create graphics.
☐ role ☐ random ☐ radius ☐ rectangle	☐ Scratch ☐ Switch ☐ Scribble ☐ Itch	☐ true ☐ false	☐ circumference ☐ diameter ☐ centre ☐ radius	☐ camera ☐ scanner ☐ printer ☐ plotter

Bitmaps

◎ Learning objectives

1. Understand what a bitmap graphic is.
2. Understand the basic structure of a bitmap.
3. Understand the link between resolution and image quality.

1. 💬 Key word definitions

Tick the word or phrase when you know its meaning.

☐ bitmap   ☐ pixel

☐ file size   ☐ pixels per inch (PPI)

☐ gradient   ☐ resolution

☐ image quality

2. Starter activity

Describe what is meant by the term 'bitmap'.

....

....

3. What is a bitmap?

Fill in the blanks, using the words below:

pixels	colour	image	detailed

A bitmap is an .... file made up of dots, or .... Each pixel can be a different .... and the more pixels there are, the more .... the image.

4. Bitmap structure

Draw a line from each term to the matching description:

pixel		relates to the number of pixels within an image
resolution		describes the change from one colour to another
gradient		short for picture elements

5. Resolution

Describe the link between resolution and image quality.

....

....

6. Image quality

Describe what will happen to the quality of an image if the physical size of a bitmap is increased.

....

....

7. Bitmap file types

List three file types that are based on bitmaps.

1. ....

2. ....

3. ....

8. Plenary quick quiz

Question 1	Question 2	Question 3	Question 4	Question 5
Which device is commonly used to create bitmap images?	Which of the following is not a bitmap file?	What is fading from black to white known as?	What does PPI stand for?	What resolution do modern games consoles have?
☐ modem ☐ router ☐ plotter ☐ camera	☐ DXF ☐ BMP ☐ JPG ☐ TIFF	☐ resolution ☐ gradient ☐ bitmap ☐ vector	☐ patterns per image ☐ pixels per image ☐ pictures per inch ☐ pixels per inch	☐ 2K ☐ 4K ☐ 8K ☐ 16K

Vectors vs bitmaps

◎ Learning objectives

1. Understand the key differences between vectors and bitmaps.
2. Consider the advantages and disadvantages of vectors and bitmaps in a given situation.

1. 💬 Key word definitions

Tick the word or phrase when you know its meaning.

- ☐ bitmap
- ☐ file size
- ☐ image quality
- ☐ photo realistic
- ☐ pixel
- ☐ resolution
- ☐ scaling
- ☐ vector

2. Starter activity

List three criteria that can be used to compare vectors and bitmaps.

1. ....
2. ....
3. ....

3. Vectors vs bitmaps

Tick each statement to show whether it applies to a bitmap or a vector.

Statement	Bitmap	Vector
Generally smaller file sizes.		
Can be resized without losing quality.		
More suitable for high quality digital photos.		
Difficult to create gradients.		
Image quality will drop if stretched.		

4. Real-world

Name a software application that can be used for vectors, and one that can be used for and bitmaps:

- Vectors: ....
- Bitmaps: ....

5. Scenarios

Tick to show whether bitmap or vector graphics would be better suited to the following scenarios.

Scenario	Bitmap	Vector
Creating a new sports logo that incorporates lots of geometric shapes.		
An outdoor adventure magazine is showing images of mountain ranges.		
A new computer operating system would like a background of flowing liquids and colour effects.		
A new children's cartoon character, made from simple lines, will need to be advertised on posters of many different sizes.		

6. Original scenarios

Create two new scenarios of your own and put them under the correct heading to show whether they should be created using bitmaps or vectors.

Scenario using bitmaps:

....

....

Scenario using vectors:

....

....

7. Plenary quick quiz

Question 1	Question 2	Question 3	Question 4	Question 5
Which of the following is not an Adobe program?	True or false? A vector can be viewed clearly at any magnification.	What does DPI stand for?	What resolution are commercial magazines recommended to use?	Which is easier?
☐ Photoshop ☐ Moviemaker ☐ Illustrator ☐ InDesign	☐ true ☐ false	☐ dots per index ☐ dimension picture index ☐ dots per inch ☐ digital pixels inch	☐ 30 dpi ☐ 300 dpi ☐ 1000 dpi ☐ 150 dpi	☐ converting a vector to a bitmap ☐ converting a bitmap to a vector

Binary and pixels

◎ Learning objectives

1. Understand the key differences between vectors and bitmaps.
2. Demonstrate how to create a simple graphic using a binary sequence.

1. 💬 Key word definitions

Tick the word or phrase when you know its meaning.

- ☐ binary
- ☐ binary word
- ☐ bitmap image
- ☐ code
- ☐ pixel
- ☐ resolution

2. Starter activity

Describe why all images must be converted to binary.

....

....

Please note: Unless otherwise stated, 1 represents black and 0 represents white in binary graphic examples.

3. Black and white images

Complete the binary table that represents the simple graphic below.

 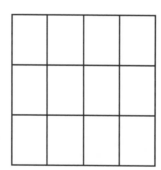

4. Defining a binary word

Describe what is meant by the term 'binary word'.

....

....

5. Binary word

Write out the binary sequence from question 3 as a binary word.

....

6. High resolution graphics

Use the following binary word to complete the image and binary table below, using white to represent zeros and black to represent ones.

> 0111111111100000001100000011111111110010000000010010110011010010110011010
> 01000000000100101000010100101111110100100000000100111111111110000000000000

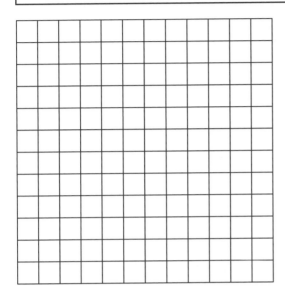 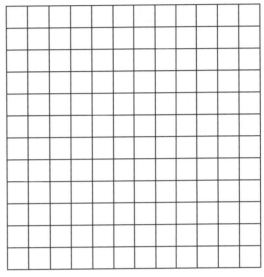

7. Plenary quick quiz

Question 1	Question 2	Question 3	Question 4	Question 5
What is a problem with bitmap fonts?	True or false? The only characters in binary are 1 and 0.	Which of the following is a binary word?	True or false? Binary grids are read from bottom to top.	What is two colour art known as?
☐ too small ☐ large files ☐ cannot be resized ☐ lack of detail	☐ true ☐ false	☐ 01010 ☐ 01010101 ☐ 111000111 ☐ All of the above	☐ true ☐ false	☐ 1-bit ☐ 2-bit ☐ 3-bit ☐ 4-bit

Colour depth and binary representation

◎ Learning objectives

1. Understand the purpose of colour depth in digital images.
2. Understand how colour depth is represented in binary.
3. Demonstrate how to represent simple colour images in binary.

1. 💬 Key word definitions

Tick the word or phrase when you know its meaning.

☐ binary	☐ bit
☐ binary word	☐ colour depth
☐ bitmap	☐ represent

2. Starter activity

Describe the meaning of the term 'colour depth'.

....

....

3. Binary bits

Describe the relationship between the number of bits and the number of colours.

....

....

4. Colour depth

Complete the gaps in the table below.

Number of bits per pixel	Number of possible colours
1	2
2	
3	8
4	
5	32
6	
7	128
8	

5. 2-bit graphics

Complete the 2-bit binary table below.

Binary		Colour
		White
0	1	Light grey
		Dark grey
		Black

6. Four colour graphic

Complete the binary table for the 6x6 section of the 2-bit image below.

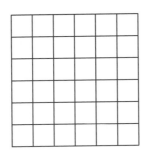 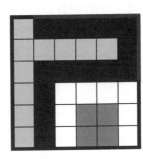

7. Increased colours

If an image increases from two colours to four, what happens to the binary word for that image?

....

8. Plenary quick quiz

Question 1	Question 2	Question 3	Question 4	Question 5
How many colours would an early 2-bit game be able to display?	True or false? Some early gaming devices used shades of green as a colour palette.	How many colours would a 9-bit image include?	What type of display do most computers and smartphones use?	True or false? A 24-bit image can include around 16 million colours.
☐ one ☐ two ☐ three ☐ four	☐ true ☐ false	☐ 256 ☐ 384 ☐ 512 ☐ 1024	☐ 8-bit ☐ 24-bit ☐ 6-bit ☐ 48-bit	☐ true ☐ false

Digital image properties

◎ Learning objectives

1. Understand the key properties of a digital image.
2. Understand the link between pixel dimensions and file size.
3. Be able to calculate the file size of a simple image.

1. 💬 Key word definitions

Tick the word or phrase when you know its meaning.

☐ binary   ☐ dimension   ☐ pixel

☐ bits   ☐ file size   ☐ pixel size

☐ colour depth   ☐ image   ☐ resolution

2. Starter activity

Draw a line from each term to the matching description.

pixel size		The number of colours each pixel can show.
dimension		The number of pixels in one square inch.
resolution		The number of pixels in total in the image.
colour depth		Height and width in pixels.

3. Formula for calculating file size

Complete the formula below to calculate the file size of an image in bits.

colour depth	pixels	file size

.... = ... × ....

4. Create a simple calculation

Use the formula from question 3 to calculate the file size in bits.

- Number of pixels: 36
- Colour depth: 2

....

....

5. Calculate the file size of a simple image

Calculate the file size in bits of this image:

....

....

....

....

6.   Calculate the file size of a complete image

Calculate the file size in bits of this image:

....

....

....

....

7.   Dimensions and file size

Describe the relationship between the number of pixels and the file size.

....

....

8.   Plenary quick quiz

Question 1	Question 2	Question 3	Question 4	Question 5
If the pixel height is 12 and the width is 10, what is the number of pixels?	How many pixels are in an image with a colour depth of 2 and file size of 48 bits?	Complete this sentence. Resolution considers the number of pixels in one square…	Colour depth uses which unit?	True or false? When printing commercially, a lo-res image is fine.
☐ 22 ☐ 2 ☐ 120 ☐ 1200	☐ 12 ☐ 24 ☐ 50 ☐ 96	☐ cm ☐ m ☐ inch ☐ km	☐ bits ☐ bytes ☐ nibbles ☐ pixels	☐ true ☐ false

Binary addition

◎ Learning objectives

1. Understand how to add two binary words together.
2. Demonstrate how to add colours together using binary equivalents.

1. 💬 Key word definitions

Tick the word or phrase when you know its meaning.

- ☐ binary
- ☐ column addition
- ☐ cyan
- ☐ denary
- ☐ hexadecimal (HEX)
- ☐ magenta
- ☐ overflow
- ☐ spectrum

2. Starter activity

List the rules for adding binary words together. The first one has been done for you.

Rule one: 0 + 0 = 0

Rule two: ....

Rule three: ....

Rule four: ....

3. Simple addition

Add the two binary words together.

1 0 1 1

0 1 0 1

4. A longer addition

Add the two binary words together.

0 1 0 1 1 0 1 1

0 0 1 0 1 1 0 1

5. Overflow

Describe the meaning of the term 'overflow' in relation to an 8-bit binary sequence.

....

....

6. Adding binary colours 1

Using the table below, add together red and green. What colour has been made?

Colour	6-bit binary
Red	11 00 00
Green	00 11 00
Blue	00 00 11
Magenta	11 00 11
Yellow	11 11 00
Cyan	00 11 11

....

....

....

....

7. Adding binary colours 2

Using the table from question 6, add together blue and red. What colour has been made?

....

....

....

....

8. Plenary quick quiz

Question 1	Question 2	Question 3	Question 4	Question 5
What is 10 in denary?	In binary addition, find: 1 + 0 =	Which of the following numbers will result in an 8-bit sequence overflow?	Which base system does hexadecimal use?	True or false? Binary numbers higher than 8-bit cannot be added together.
☐ 1	☐ 0	☐ 253	☐ 16	☐ true
☐ 2	☐ 1	☐ 254	☐ 8	☐ false
☐ 4	☐ 2	☐ 255	☐ 32	
☐ 8	☐ –1	☐ 256	☐ 4	

Unit 1: Short answer questions

1. A typical 4-mark question

You have been asked to create a logo for a new photography business. The logo needs to include a high-quality photo and will be printed commercially.

Describe whether you would use bitmap or vector software to create the logo. Give three reasons for your choice.

2. Another 4-mark question

As a smartphone app programmer, it is important to know the size of the files you are creating.

Write the formula used to calculate a file size in bits. Then, calculate the size of the following image:

- Image size: 20 pixels wide, 10 pixels high
- Colour depth: 3

✏ Revision checklist

	MIND-MAP	MISSING WORDS	WRITE A QUIZ	FLASHCARDS	COVER AND WRITE
U1 L1 – Vector graphics					
U1 L2 – Creating a vector graphic					
U1 L3 – Bitmaps					
U1 L4 – Vectors vs bitmaps					
U1 L5 – Binary and pixels					
U1 L6 – Colour depth and binary representation					
U1 L7 & 8 – Digital image properties					
U1 L9 & 10 – Binary addition					

Bits, bytes and nibbles

◎ Learning objectives

1. Understand the purpose of a storage device.
2. Understand the terms bits, bytes and nibbles in terms of storage capacity.
3. Demonstrate an ability to calculate the file size of simple graphics.

1. 💬 Key word definitions

Tick the word or phrase when you know its meaning.

☐ binary ☐ pixel

☐ bit ☐ storage

☐ byte

☐ nibble

2. Starter activity

Describe the purpose of a storage device.

....

....

3. Storage devices

Draw a line from each storage device to the matching description.

internal hard drive		Used to add storage to smartphones and cameras.
flash drive		Used to add additional storage to computers.
memory cards		Non-removable storage inside a computer.
external hard drive		Used to transport files from one computer to another.

4. Bits, bytes and nibbles

Complete the statements below. All values relate to an 8-bit binary number, for example, 11111100.

1 byte   = ... bits

4 bits   = ... nibble

2 nibbles   = ... byte

5. Text file sizes

Complete the table below. Tip: 1 letter = 1 byte

Word	Bytes	Nibbles	Bits
cat			
bubble			
elephant			
skateboard			

6. Calculating file sizes

Complete the formula below using the terms provided.

pixels	file size in byte	colour depth

$$= \frac{(\qquad \times \qquad)}{8}$$

7. Calculating a 3-bit image file size

Calculate the file size in bytes of the image described below.

A 4-bit colour image.
Pixel size = height: 10, width: 5

....

....

....

....

8. Plenary quick quiz

Question 1	Question 2	Question 3	Question 4	Question 5
True or false? 1 nibble = byte.	Which can be used to add more storage space to a tablet?	One of the oldest examples of storage media is the…?	The word 'smartphone' would require how many bytes to store it?	True or false? There are 8 bits in 1 byte.
☐ true ☐ false	☐ internal drive ☐ flash drive ☐ memory card ☐ external hard drive	☐ CD-ROM ☐ floppy disc ☐ USB ☐ drive ☐ printer	☐ 40 ☐ 30 ☐ 20 ☐ 10	☐ true ☐ false

Storage capacity

◉ Learning objectives

1. Understand the need for larger file storage capacity.
2. Define larger storage in terms of kibi-, mebi- and gibibytes.
3. Demonstrate the ability to calculate larger file sizes.

1. 💬 Key word definitions

Tick the word or phrase when you know its meaning.

☐ base 2   ☐ gigibyte (GiB)
☐ base 10   ☐ kibibyte (KiB)
☐ binary   ☐ kilobyte (KB)
☐ data storage   ☐ mebibyte (MiB)
☐ gigabyte (GB)

2. Starter activity

Describe two types of file that a family might store electronically.

1. ....

2. ....

3. Base 2 data storage

Draw a line from the storage unit to its equivalent size.

1 kibibyte (KiB)		1024 mebibytes
1 mebibyte (MiB)		1024 bytes
1 gibibyte (GiB)		1024 kibibytes

4. Base 10 data storage

Draw a line from the storage unit to its equivalent size.

1 kilobyte (KB)		1000 kilobytes
1 megabyte (MB)		1000 megabytes
1 gigabyte (GB)		1000 bytes

5. Number bases

Describe the difference between using base 2, rather than base 10, to calculate storage.

....

....

6. Converting small file sizes

Convert the following files from bytes to kibibytes.

File	bytes	kibibytes (KiB)
Text	2048	
Vector graphic	512	
Spreadsheet	5120	

7. Converting large file sizes

Convert the following files from kibibytes to bytes.

File	kibibytes (KiB)	bytes
Image	10	
Audio	6	
Video	100	

8. Plenary quick quiz

Question 1	Question 2	Question 3	Question 4	Question 5
What is 2^{10} equal to?	True or false? KiB and MiB are base 10 units.	What does the IEC stand for?	True or false? Base 10 storage units cannot calculate the number of binary bits.	What is the base 2 unit equal to 2^{80} called?
☐ 2000 bytes ☐ 1024 bytes ☐ 1000 bytes ☐ 20 bytes	☐ true ☐ false	☐ international electrotechnical commission ☐ internet electrical commission ☐ internal energy computer ☐ independent electrotechnical company	☐ true ☐ false	☐ yudabyte ☐ yodabyte ☐ yemibyte ☐ yobibyte

Binary and denary

◎ Learning objectives

1. Understand the key differences between base 2 and base 10.
2. Demonstrate how to present denary and binary numbers.
3. Understand how to convert binary to denary and vice-versa.
4. Demonstrate use of place tables and indices.

1. 💬 Key word definitions

Tick the word or phrase when you know its meaning.

☐ base 2   ☐ denary

☐ base 10   ☐ place value grid

☐ binary   ☐ power of

☐ central processing unit (CPU)

2. Starter activity

List the digits used by the base 2 and base 10 number systems.

Base 2: ....

Base 10: ....

3. Matching denary numbers

Draw a line from the power of 10 to the matching denary number.

10^6		Hundreds
10^4		Millions
10^2		Tens of thousands

4. Finding denary numbers

Complete the table for the two numbers below.

Power	10^6	10^5	10^4	10^3	10^2	10^1	10^0
	Millions	Hundreds of thousands	Tens of thousands	Thousands	Hundreds	Tens	Ones
1974							
650456							

5. Power of ten

Complete the table for the two numbers below.

Power	2^7	2^6	2^5	2^4	2^3	2^2	2^1	2^0
Description	128	64	32	16	8	4	2	1
58								
129								

6. Denary to binary

Convert the following numbers from denary to binary:

161: ....

37: ....

240: ....

7. Binary to denary

Convert the following numbers from binary to denary:

01010100:

....

11011011:

....

11100011:

....

8. Plenary quick quiz

Question 1	Question 2	Question 3	Question 4	Question 5
True or false? Binary only uses the digits 0, 1 and 2.	Base 10 was probably based on our number of...?	Using base 2, what is 2^6 equal to?	A popular way to think about 8-bit binary is as eight different...?	The CPU is made up of millions of...?
☐ true ☐ false	☐ eyes ☐ bones ☐ fingers ☐ teeth	☐ 126 ☐ 64 ☐ 16 ☐ 4	☐ switches ☐ lamps ☐ doors ☐ buttons	☐ resistors ☐ capacitors ☐ batteries ☐ transistors

Creating a 'power of' calculator

◎ Learning objectives

1. Understand the requirements of a simple algorithmic calculator.
2. Demonstrate an ability to create a simple visual-coding calculator.
3. Demonstrate an ability to create a simple calculator using Python.

1. 💬 Key word definitions

Tick the word or phrase when you know its meaning.

☐ denary   ☐ Scratch

☐ input   ☐ sprite

☐ output   ☐ variables

☐ power of

2. Starter activity

Describe the purpose of the program called Scratch.

....

....

3. Scratch commands

Draw a line from the Scratch block to the matching description.

ask		displays a message on screen
say		concatenates two strings
join		asks the user to type in a value

4. Python variable

Describe the purpose of a variable in Python.

....

....

5. Python power calculator

Look at the example of a Python program below.

```
userInput = int(input("Please enter your first number: "))
power = int(input("Please enter the power:"))
output = user Input**power
print("The resulting denary number is: ", output)
```

i) What is the purpose of the int function in lines 1 and 2?

....

....

ii) What is the purpose of the characters ** in line 3?

....

....

iii) What would be the resulting output if the following are typed into the input commands:

- Line 1: 2
- Line 2: 4

....

....

6. Plenary quick quiz

Question 1	Question 2	Question 3	Question 4	Question 5
True or false? There is no specific power of function in Scratch.	What is a useful source of online help for any program called?	What are the characters on screen in Scratch called?	Adding a capital letter within a variable firstName is an example of a...?	Using Python, what would be the result of 2**3?
☐ true ☐ false	☐ cookie ☐ terms and conditions document ☐ forum ☐ credit	☐ sprites ☐ spots ☐ signs ☐ signals	☐ operator ☐ naming convention ☐ integer ☐ bookmark	☐ 5 ☐ 8 ☐ 16 ☐ 1

Internet bandwidth

◎ Learning objectives

1. Understand the concept of bandwidth.
2. Demonstrate an ability to calculate internet file transfer speeds.
3. Understand the term 'bandwidth bottleneck'.

1. 💬 Key word definitions

Tick the word or phrase when you know its meaning.

☐ bandwidth	☐ file size	☐ network
☐ bits	☐ kibibyte (KiB)	☐ routers
☐ byte	☐ mebibyte (MiB)	☐ transfer
☐ data	☐ megabits (MB)	

2. Starter activity

Describe the meaning of the term 'bandwidth'.

....

....

3. Bits, bytes and nibbles

Complete the statements below. All values relate to base 2 units.

3 bytes   =   bits
8 bits   =   bytes
2 mebibytes   =   kibibytes

4. Calculating file transfer speeds

Complete the formula below, using the terms provided.

file size   file transfer speed   bandwidth

.... = ... / ....

5. Typical file transfer speeds

Complete the table below of typical file sizes and file transfer speeds

File	Time to download (seconds)	
	Bandwidth = 2 MiB	Bandwidth = 10 MiB
8 MiB email attachment		
10 MiB audio file		
100 MiB video clip		

6. Bandwidth bottleneck

Describe the meaning of the term 'bandwidth bottleneck'.

....

....

7. Bottleneck example

Look at the diagram of a bandwidth bottleneck below. What will the bandwidth speed become between the web server and the computer?

....

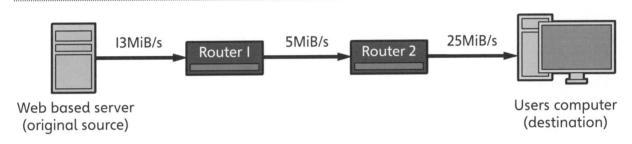

13MiB/s   Router 1   5MiB/s   Router 2   25MiB/s

Web based server
(original source)

Users computer
(destination)

8. Plenary quick quiz

Question 1	Question 2	Question 3	Question 4	Question 5
What does bps stand for?	True or false? 8 bytes = 1 bit.	Over the last ten years, how many times has the worldwide average bandwidth speed multiplied?	What is MiB short for?	True or false? A router connects networks together.
☐ beats per second ☐ bits per session ☐ bits per second ☐ bytes per system	☐ true ☐ false	☐ 5 ☐ 10 ☐ 15 ☐ 25	☐ mebibytes ☐ megabits ☐ masterbots ☐ megibits	☐ true ☐ false

Creating a bandwidth calculator

◎ Learning objectives

1. Understand the requirements of a simple file transfer calculator.
2. Demonstrate an ability to create a simple visual-coding calculator.
3. Demonstrate an ability to create a simple calculator using Python.

1. 💬 Key word definitions

Tick the word or phrase when you know its meaning.

☐ bandwidth   ☐ program

☐ concatenate   ☐ Python

☐ data   ☐ Scratch

☐ inputs   ☐ test table

☐ integers   ☐ transfer

☐ output   ☐ variable

2. Starter activity

Draw a line from the Scratch block to the matching description.

when 'Flag' is clicked		wait until an input is responded to
set		start the program running
ask and wait		assign a value to a variable

3. Scratch program

Look at the example Scratch program below. It calculates the time it takes for a file to download. Circle the three variables in the program.

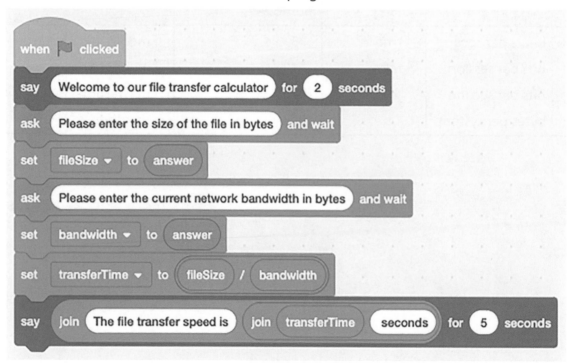

4. Python program

Look at the example Python program below. It calculates the time it takes for a file to download.

```
fileSize = int(input("Please enter the size of the file in bytes: "))
bandwidth = int(input("Please enter the current network bandwidth in bytes:"))
transferTime = fileSize/bandwidth
print("The resulting file transfer speed is:", transferTime, " seconds")
```

i) Why is it important that the responses to lines 1 and 2 are both in bytes?

....

....

ii) What is the purpose of the / symbol in line 3?

....

....

iii) What would the output be if the following are typed into the input commands?

- Line 1: 20 ....

- Line 2: 4 ....

5. Test tables

Describe the purpose of a test table.

....

....

6. Plenary quick quiz

Question 1	Question 2	Question 3	Question 4	Question 5
What is file transfer speed measured in?	True or false? Variables are not case-sensitive.	After testing and editing, what is it important to do?	What is the symbol used to separate a quote in the print line and a variable?	In a test table, what is the column after an expected result called?
☐ hours ☐ minutes ☐ seconds ☐ milliseconds	☐ true ☐ false	☐ delete data ☐ start again ☐ rename ☐ retest	☐ full stop ☐ comma ☐ colon ☐ question mark	☐ actual result ☐ changes required ☐ estimated result ☐ false result

Compression

◎ Learning objectives

1 Understand the purpose of compression.
2. Understand the difference between lossy and lossless compression.
3. Demonstrate an understanding of choosing the most appropriate compression choice for a given scenario.

1. 💬 Key word definitions

Tick the word or phrase when you know its meaning.

- ☐ compression
- ☐ lossless
- ☐ decompress
- ☐ lossy

2. Starter activity

Describe the meaning of the term 'file compression'.

....

....

3. Uses of file compression

List three uses of file compression.

1. ....

2. ....

3. ....

4. Lossy compression

Complete the statement below, using the words provided.

Lossy compression .... part of the file, ... the file size, but when the file is ...., the deleted parts cannot be restored. Lossy compression is never used for .... as characters would be lost, but it is often used for image and .... files.

| decompressed | sound | deletes | text files | reducing |

5. Lossy and lossless compression

Describe the difference between lossy and lossless compression.

....

....

....

6. Scenarios

Tick whether the scenarios below should use lossy or lossless compression.

Scenario	Lossy	Lossless
a customer database of personal details		
a wedding album of photos		
a music album recorded in a studio		
adding an audio clip to a social network site		
a snapshot sent within an instant messaging app		

7. Image compression

Describe three settings that can be used when adjusting image compression.

1. ....

2. ....

3. ....

8. Plenary quick quiz

Question 1	Question 2	Question 3	Question 4	Question 5
Which of the following does not use lossy compression?	True or false? An MP3 file often deletes the sounds we cannot hear.	What is the number of pixels in one inch referred to as?	True or false? When compressed, lossy data can still be recovered.	True or false? Lossy compression creates smaller file sizes than lossless compression.
☐ TXT ☐ JPEG ☐ MP3 ☐ MP4	☐ true ☐ false	☐ depth ☐ layers ☐ resolution ☐ detail	☐ true ☐ false	☐ true ☐ false

Run length encoding

◎ Learning objectives

1. Understand the purpose of run length encoding.
2. Understand the link between run length encoding and binary pixels.
3. Demonstrate an ability to compress a simple graphic using run length encoding.

1. 💬 Key word definitions

Tick the word or phrase when you know its meaning.

- ☐ bits
- ☐ compress
- ☐ decompress
- ☐ encoding
- ☐ pixels
- ☐ run length encoding

2. Starter activity

Describe the purpose of run length encoding.

....

....

....

3. Image data

State two pieces of information required to calculate the initial file size of an image before using run length encoding.

1. ....

2. ....

4. Compressing a simple image

Look at the simple 1-bit graphic below and complete the table.

Note: b = black, w = white.

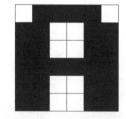

w	b	b	b	b	w
b	b	w	w	b	b
b	b	w	w	b	b
b	b	b	b	b	b
b	b	w	w	b	b
b	b	w	w	b	b

Original string	Size in bytes	RLE version	New size in bytes
wbbbbw	6		
bbwwbb	6		
bbwwbb	6		
bbbbbb	6		
bbwwbb	6		
bbwwbb	6		
Total file size	36		

5. Create your own graphic

Create your own 1-bit graphic. Then complete the table and apply run length encoding.

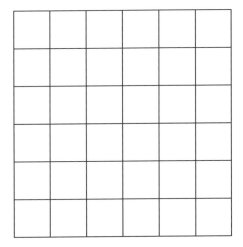

Original string	Size in bytes	RLE version	New size in bytes
Total file size			

6. Plenary quick quiz

Question 1	Question 2	Question 3	Question 4	Question 5
True or false? Run length encoding is a lossy compression method.	How many bytes would the word 'banana' require?	How many colours can a 1-bit graphic have?	Using ASCII, how many bytes is each character?	True or false? Run length encoding does not make every file smaller.
☐ true ☐ false	☐ 5 ☐ 6 ☐ 7 ☐ 8	☐ 4 ☐ 3 ☐ 2 ☐ 1	☐ 1 ☐ 2 ☐ 4 ☐ 8	☐ true ☐ false

Unit 2: Short answer questions

1. A typical 4-mark question

You are a reporter writing about the impact of technology on society. The section you are witing is about the increasing need for more storage.

Describe two examples of why a family might need to store more data. For each example, state a typical file size unit.

....

....

....

....

....

....

2. Another 4-mark question

Working for a library, you have been asked to try and reduce the size of a digital archive.

You have suggested run length encoding.

Describe how run length encoding works and provide a very simple example using the sequence: AAAAABBBCCCC

....

....

....

....

....

....

✏ Revision checklist

	MIND-MAP	MISSING WORDS	WRITE A QUIZ	FLASHCARDS	COVER AND WRITE
U2 L1 – Bits, bytes and nibbles					
U2 L2 – Storage capacity					
U2 L3 – Binary and denary					
U2 L4 – Creating a 'power of' calculator					
U2 L5 – Internet bandwidth					
U2 L6 – Creating a bandwidth calculator					
U2 L7 & 8 – Compression					
U2 L9 & 10 – Run length encoding					

Computer hardware

◎ Learning objectives

1. Understand the difference between hardware and software.
2. Understand the main components of a computer.
3. Understand the common elements of different devices.

1. 💬 Key word definitions

Tick the word or phrase when you know its meaning.

☐ central processing unit (CPU)   ☐ power supply unit (PSU)

☐ hard drive   ☐ sound card

☐ memory   ☐ storage

☐ motherboard   ☐ video card

2. Starter activity

Describe the difference between hardware and software.

....

....

....

3. Types of computer

List three different types of computer.

1. ....

2. ....

3. ....

4. Computer components

Draw a line from the components to the matching description.

central processing unit		provides the correct power supply to all components
memory		the main storage device, storing the operating system
power supply unit		the short-term memory, it stores program data and the results from calculations
hard drive		the brain of the computer, it carries out all processing

5. Motherboard

Describe the role of the motherboard in a modern computer.

....

....

....

....

6. Scenarios

Tick the most important component for the tasks below.

Scenario	Video card	Hard drive	Central processing unit
Playing the latest 3D computer game.			
Carrying out complex numerical modelling.			
Organising family files and images.			

7. Plenary quick quiz

Question 1	Question 2	Question 3	Question 4	Question 5
True or false? A smart television is not a type of computer.	Which of the following is not software?	Which body part is the central processing unit often described as?	In which component is short term memory stored?	Which of these is an example of a low-cost, tiny computer?
☐ true ☐ false	☐ word processor ☐ spreadsheet ☐ mouse ☐ CAD	☐ eyes ☐ ears ☐ mouth ☐ brain	☐ CD-ROM ☐ RAM ☐ PSU ☐ CPPU	☐ Raspberry Pi ☐ Pineapple Pi ☐ Strawberry Pi ☐ Apple Pi

Wearable technology

◎ Learning objectives

1. Understand the concept of wearable technology.
2. Be able to describe some of the components used in wearable technology.
3. Be able to describe some of the advantages and disadvantages of wearable technology.

1. 💬 Key word definitions

Tick the word or phrase when you know its meaning.

- ☐ augmented reality (AR)
- ☐ sensors
- ☐ virtual reality (VR)
- ☐ wearable technology

2. Starter activity

Describe what is meant by the term 'wearable technology'.

....

....

....

....

3. Wearable technology

List three examples of wearable technology.

1. ....

2. ....

3. ....

4. Functionality of wearable technology

Draw a line from the functionality to the matching description.

augmented and virtual reality		messaging and social network notifications
fitness tracking		replacing everything we see via a headset or adding additional information to our field of view
payments		making contactless payments without the need for cash or a credit card
communication		monitoring the location, movement and the health of the wearer

5. Power supply

Describe why batteries are a concern in wearable technology.

....

....

6. Benefits and drawbacks of wearable technology

Tick whether the following are a potential benefit or a drawback to wearable technology.

Statement	Benefit	Drawback
New technology is often very expensive.		
Video games could be more interactive.		
Our location is being shared online more often.		
Health problems could be discovered.		

7. The future of wearable technology

List three examples of potential future wearable technology.

1. ....

2. ....

3. ....

8. Plenary quick quiz

Question 1	Question 2	Question 3	Question 4	Question 5
What does AR stand for?	How often do some wearable devices need charging?	Which of the following is not related to fitness tracking?	What is virtual reality normally fitted to?	True or false? Future technology may be implanted under the skin.
☐ action reality ☐ audio realism ☐ augmented reality ☐ augmented realism	☐ every hour ☐ every day ☐ every month ☐ every year	☐ heart-rate ☐ speed ☐ calorie counting ☐ text messaging	☐ a headset ☐ a watch ☐ a shoe ☐ a t-shirt	☐ true ☐ false

Logo design

Learning objectives

1. Understand the purpose of a logo.
2. Understand the key components of a logo.
3. Understand some of the rules of good logo design technology.

1. 💬 Key word definitions

Tick the word or phrase when you know its meaning.

☐ bitmaps   ☐ marketing

☐ brand   ☐ transferability

☐ logo   ☐ vectors

2. Starter activity

Describe the purpose of a logo.

....

....

3. Why do we need logos?

List two scenarios where a new logo might be used.

1. ....

2. ....

4. Logo components

Describe three key components of any new logo design.

1. ....

2. ....

3. ....

5. Logo design rules

Draw a line from the rule to the matching question.

construction		Does the full name need to be included, or its initials? Are there images already associated with the brand?
transferability		Can the logo be easily transferred to other documents or products?
content		What must be included in the design and is there an existing house style?
text or graphic based		Will the logo be made using bitmaps or vectors?

6. Transferability

Describe two reasons why a logo might need to be transferred into multiple formats.

1. ....

2. ....

7. Bitmaps and vectors

Describe one advantage and one disadvantage of constructing a logo from bitmaps or vectors.

Graphic	Advantage	Disadvantage
Bitmap		
Vector		

8. Plenary quick quiz

Question 1	Question 2	Question 3	Question 4	Question 5
Which of the following would not normally need a new logo?	True or false? A logo must contain both text and graphics.	Which of the following is not part of a house style?	Which of the following would be most suitable for a logo containing a photo?	Which of the following would be most suitable for a logo made from simple shapes?
☐ a new game ☐ a homework project ☐ a new business ☐ a new political party	☐ true ☐ false	☐ font choices ☐ colour choices ☐ an address ☐ related imagery	☐ bitmap ☐ vector	☐ bitmap ☐ vector

Introduction to spreadsheets

◎ Learning objectives

1. Understand the purpose of a spreadsheet.
2. Understand the key features of spreadsheet software.
3. Demonstrate knowledge of common spreadsheet formatting functions and tools.

1. 💬 Key word definitions

Tick the word or phrase when you know its meaning.

☐ alignment   ☐ formatting   ☐ spreadsheet

☐ border   ☐ formulas   ☐ value

☐ cell   ☐ graphs   ☐ worksheet

☐ column   ☐ merging

☐ data   ☐ rows

2. Starter activity

Describe the purpose of a spreadsheet.

....

....

....

3. Why do we need spreadsheets?

List three practical uses of spreadsheets.

1. ....

2. ....

3. ....

4. Spreadsheet features

List three features common to most spreadsheet applications.

1. ....

2. ....

3. ....

5. Formatting tools

Draw a line from the formatting tool to the matching description.

text		text can be aligned to the centre or to a specific corner of a cell
border		cells can be merged together into one
alignment		changing the size, colour, font and style of text
cell merging		changing the lines around the edge of each cell

6. Data types

In the table below, give an example of each type of data.

Data type	Example
Number	
Currency	
Percentage	
Date	
Time	

7. Scenario

List two data types which might be used in a spreadsheet showing monthly salaries.

1. ....

2. ....

8. Plenary quick quiz

Question 1	Question 2	Question 3	Question 4	Question 5
Which of the following is not a spreadsheet application?	True or false? Rows are horizontal and columns are vertical.	Combining cells above a table is an example of which formatting tool?	What is each page within a spreadsheet called?	True or false? Most spreadsheets can only display one currency.
☐ Microsoft Excel ☐ Google Sheets ☐ Adobe Acrobat ☐ Apple Numbers	☐ true ☐ false	☐ merge ☐ alignment ☐ bullets ☐ font size	☐ slide ☐ page ☐ layer ☐ worksheet	☐ true ☐ false

Spreadsheet formulas and functions

◎ Learning objectives

1. Understand the purpose of formulas and functions in spreadsheet software.
2. Understand the importance of cell referencing in spreadsheets.
3. Demonstrate understanding of a range of common formulas and functions.

1. 💬 Key word definitions

Tick the word or phrase when you know its meaning.

☐ AVERAGE	☐ function
☐ cell	☐ MAX
☐ cell referencing	☐ MIN
☐ equals sign	☐ SUM
☐ formula	☐ worksheet

2. Starter activity

Describe the purpose of using formulas and functions within a spreadsheet.

....

....

3. Cell referencing

Add the correct cell references to the highlighted cells.

	A	B	C	D	E
1					
2					
3					
4					
5					
6					

4. Using operators in spreadsheets

Complete the table below.

Operator	Description
+	Add
–	
/	
*	
=	

5. Spreadsheet functions

Draw a line from the function to the matching description.

MAX		displays the lowest value in the range of cells
MIN		displays the average value of all the values in the range of cells
SUM		displays the highest value in the range of cells
AVERAGE		displays the total of all the values in the range of cells

6. Examples of formulas and functions

Look at the spreadsheet below. Fill in the value of each of the cells in the table.

	A	B	C	D	E
1		6	12	=B1+C1	2
2		3	7	=B2*B2	4
3		5	3	=B3-C3	6
4		2	2	=B4/C4	1
5				=SUM(E1:E4)	
6				=AVERAGE(E1:E4)	
7				=MIN(E1:E4)	
8				=MAX(E1:E4)	
Cell	Value				

D1	
D2	
D3	
D4	
E5	
E6	
E7	
E8	

7. Plenary quick quiz

Question 1	Question 2	Question 3	Question 4	Question 5
True or false? Cell referencing is always a number, then a letter.	What is a colon between two cell references used to denote?	Where would the cell range C7:E7 appear?	True or false? A cell reference such as A8 can be used without a formula.	Which of the following is a popular game that uses cell references?
☐ true ☐ false	☐ a pair of cells ☐ a range of cells ☐ missing cells ☐ deleted cells	☐ horizontally ☐ vertically ☐ diagonally ☐ inverted	☐ true ☐ false	☐ Solitaire ☐ Hide and seek ☐ Snap ☐ Battleships

Spreadsheet modelling

◎ Learning objectives

1. Understand how spreadsheet modelling can be used to model real life situations.
2. Demonstrate understanding through the creation of a simple spreadsheet model.
3. Demonstrate an understanding of the terms 'what if scenario' and 'goal seek'.

1. 💬 Key word definitions

Tick the word or phrase when you know its meaning.

☐ AVERAGE	☐ MIN
☐ equals sign	☐ model
☐ formula	☐ profit
☐ function	☐ SUM
☐ goal seek	☐ *what if* scenarios
☐ MAX	

2. Starter activity

Describe the purpose of a spreadsheet model.

....

....

....

3. Why do we need spreadsheet models?

List two practical uses for a spreadsheet model.

1. ....

2. ....

4. A simple numerical model

Look at the spreadsheet model below, showing how many potential new members could be added each month to a sports club over one year. Add the missing formulas in the highlighted cells.

	A	B	C	D	E
1	Month	New members			
2	Jan	3			
3	Feb	3			
4	Mar	4			
5	Apr	4			

6	May	5			
7	Jun	5		Potential total	
8	Jul	5		Annual target	150
9	Aug	10		Members needed	
10	Sep	15		Average	
11	Oct	10		Lowest	
12	Nov	25		Highest	
13	Dec	30			

5. What if scenario

If the sports club in question 4 decided to add eight members in August instead of ten, which cells would now change?

....

6. Goal seek

Describe the purpose of the goal seek function.

....

....

7. Plenary quick quiz

Question 1	Question 2	Question 3	Question 4	Question 5
Which part of a business model does profit or loss relate to?	What is another word used for a spending limit?	True or false? The formula: =A1+A2+A3 is the same as: =SUM(A1:A3).	Target and Current Value are elements of which function?	What tool is used to set the text to the centre of a column?
☐ money generated ☐ number of items ☐ the date ☐ the month	☐ income ☐ loss ☐ average ☐ budget	☐ true ☐ false	☐ average ☐ quantity ☐ goal seek ☐ data type	☐ alignment ☐ merge ☐ fill ☐ autofill

Environmental impact of technology

◎ Learning objectives

1. Understand the effects of increased use of technology on our environment.
2. Understand what impact material and energy use has on our environment.
3. Understand the effect of electronic waste disposal on our environment.
4. Understand some of the ways we can reduce the environmental damage caused by technology.

1. 💬 Key word definitions

Tick the word or phrase when you know its meaning.

☐ electronic waste   ☐ rechargeable

☐ hazardous   ☐ recycling

☐ hibernate   ☐ toxic

☐ landfill

2. Starter activity

Draw a line from the technological impact to the related imaginary quotes.

material choices		"Mum, I need more plug sockets in my room!"
energy use		"I can't believe last year's model is now updated- I want the new one!"
electronic waste		"I never knew this phone had gold in it!"

3. Material choices

List three materials that cannot be replaced or are difficult to create.

1. ....

2. ....

3. ....

4. Energy use

Describe three examples of why technology increases our energy requirements.

1. ....

2. ....

3. ....

5. Electronic waste

Describe three problems caused by electronic waste.

1. ....

2. ....

3. ....

6. Preventing environmental damage

Complete the table below, adding two potential solutions to each concern.

Material choices	Energy use	Electronic waste

7. Trade-in programmes

Describe how trade-in programmes can help to reduce electronic waste.

....

....

8. Plenary quick quiz

Question 1	Question 2	Question 3	Question 4	Question 5
Which of these is not a rare element?	True or false? Batteries often contain toxic materials.	True or false? A large amount of technology in landfill sites is still usable.	Which of the following is not a renewable energy resource?	Replacing components rather than disposing of them is also known as…?
☐ gold ☐ silver ☐ sand ☐ palladium	☐ true ☐ false	☐ true ☐ false	☐ solar ☐ wind ☐ water ☐ gas	☐ hibernation ☐ upgradability ☐ dependability ☐ durability

Presenting data in an informative way

◎ Learning objectives

1. Understand how data can be presented in a visual way.
2. Understand the importance of presenting data in an informative and interesting way.
3. Understand the purpose of an infographic.

1. 💬 Key word definitions

Tick the word or phrase when you know its meaning.

☐ chart   ☐ infographic

☐ data   ☐ labels

☐ graph

2. Starter activity

Describe the purpose of a chart or graph.

....

....

....

3. Types of chart

Draw a line from the chart to the matching description.

pie		ideal for showing changing values over time
line		displays the value of a range of similar items against the same quantity
bar/column		displays two sets of data to see if there is a connection between them
scatter		ideal for showing individual parts of a whole or percentages

4. Chart examples

Label each chart with the correct name.

 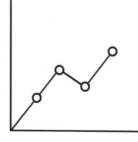 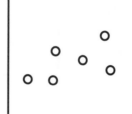 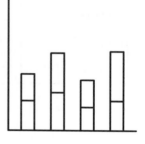

....

5. Infographics

Explain what an infographic is.

....

....

....

6. How infographics are used

Give three uses of an infographic.

1. ....

2. ....

3. ....

7. Infographic components

List three elements that can be used to create an infographic.

1. ....

2. ....

3. ....

8. Plenary quick quiz

Question 1	Question 2	Question 3	Question 4	Question 5
Which chart is best for showing the share of votes in a competition?	Which chart is best for comparing the price of different smartphones?	True or false? The term 'infographic' combines the word information and graphic.	Which of the following are often used to visualise historical events?	True or false? By changing the scale, axis and labels of a chart, the meaning can be changed.
☐ line ☐ pie ☐ bar/column ☐ scatter	☐ line ☐ pie ☐ bar/column ☐ scatter	☐ true ☐ false	☐ charts ☐ bullet points ☐ diagrams ☐ timelines	☐ true ☐ false

Surveys and questionnaires

◎ Learning objectives

1. Understand the purpose of collecting user data.
2. Understand how surveys are used.
3. Understand the importance of good question techniques.
4. Understand the difference between qualitative and quantitative data.

1. 💬 Key word definitions

Tick the word or phrase when you know its meaning.

☐ bias	☐ reliability
☐ leading question	☐ sample size
☐ qualitative	☐ survey
☐ quantitative	☐ unreliable
☐ questionnaire	

2. Starter activity

Give two examples of when user data might be collected.

1. ....

2. ....

3. Surveys

Describe three ways a question-based survey might be carried out.

1. ....

2. ....

3. ....

4. Questioning techniques

Draw a line from the things to consider when writing questions to the matching description.

audience		Are the questions over-complicated, and could they result in poor responses?
confusion		Are the right number of people being consulted?
language		Are you talking to the right people, and will they be interested in the topic?
sample size		Are any questions written in a clear, simple way using words suitable for all?

5. Bias

Explain what the term 'bias' means, and why it is important to think about when writing questions.

....

....

....

6. Examples of qualitative and quantitative data

In the table below, tick whether the data listed is qualitative or quantitative.

Statement	Qualitative	Quantitative
Interviews		
Yes/No questions		
Multiple choice		
Group discussions		
Observations		
Star or number rating		

7. Plenary quick quiz

Question 1	Question 2	Question 3	Question 4	Question 5
Which of the following examples is normally carried out in person?	What does sample size normally relate to?	Which of these is another word for a biased question?	A sliding scale is an example of collecting…?	True or false? Qualitative data is always more important to collect than quantitative data.
☐ website survey ☐ interview ☐ video call ☐ telephone call	☐ question difficulty ☐ the age of the person ☐ the number of people questioned ☐ the language used	☐ leading question ☐ multiple choice question ☐ yes/no question ☐ easy question	☐ qualitative data ☐ quantitative data	☐ true ☐ false

Advanced spreadsheet functions

◎ Learning objectives

1. Demonstrate understanding of the COUNT and COUNTIF function.
2. Understand the importance of appropriately formatted charts.

1. 💬 Key word definitions

Tick the word or phrase when you know its meaning.

☐ axis   ☐ criteria   ☐ function

☐ COUNT   ☐ formatting

☐ COUNTIF   ☐ formula

2. Starter activity

Describe the purpose of the COUNT function in a spreadsheet.

....

....

3. COUNTIF function

Describe the purpose of the COUNTIF function in a spreadsheet.

....

....

4. COUNT function example

Look at the spreadsheet below.

	A	B	C	D
1	**Food**			=COUNT(A2:A6)
2	Pizza			
3	Fish			
4	Bagel			
5	Paella			
6	Curry			

i) What value will appear in cell D1?

....

....

ii) Why does the formula in cell D1 not include cell A1?

....

....

5. COUNTIF function example

Look at the spreadsheet below.

	A	B	C	D
1	**Food**			=COUNTIF(A2:A6,"Pizza")
2	Pizza			
3	Bagel			
4	Bagel			
5	Paella			
6	Curry			
7	Pizza			

i) What value will appear in cell D1?

....

....

ii) Rewrite the formula in cell D1 to count the number of bagels.

....

....

6. Formatting charts

List three things that are important to consider when formatting a chart or graph.

1. ....

2. ....

3. ....

7. Plenary quick quiz

Question 1	Question 2	Question 3	Question 4	Question 5
Which function is ideal for recording a repeating value in a list?	True or false? The COUNT function adds the totals of the values selected.	What is the range and value in a COUNTIF function separated by?	How is the Y axis in a chart normally shown?	True or false? Only pie charts can be visualised in 3D.
☐ COUNT ☐ COUNTIF ☐ MAX ☐ SUM	☐ true ☐ false	☐ colon ☐ question mark ☐ comma ☐ quotation mark	☐ horizontally ☐ vertically ☐ diagonally ☐ inverted	☐ true ☐ false

Unit 3: Short answer questions

1. A typical 4-mark question

You have been asked to create a new logo for a social media site. Before creating the new logo, you remind yourself of some simple design rules to follow.

Describe two of these rules and give an explanation of each one.

2. Another 4-mark question

Before launching a new social media site, surveys are being carried out to find what features people would like to see. A mixture of qualitative and quantitative data questions are being included.

Describe the difference between qualitative and quantitative data and provide an example of each.

✏️ Revision checklist

	MIND-MAP	MISSING WORDS	WRITE A QUIZ	FLASHCARDS	COVER AND WRITE
U3 L1 Computer hardware					
U3 L2 Wearable technology					
U3 L3 Logo design					
U3 L4 Introduction to spreadsheets					
U3 L5 Spreadsheet formulas and functions					
U3 L6 Spreadsheet modelling					
U3 L7 Environmental impact of technology					
U3 L8 Presenting data in an informative way					
U3 L9 Surveys and questionnaires					
U3 L10 Advanced spreadsheet functions					

Social media

◎ Learning objectives

1. Understand the term social media.
2. Understand the different types of social media and the features of each type.
3. Understand some of the advantages and disadvantages of social networking.

1. 💬 Key word definitions

Tick the word or phrase when you know its meaning.

☐ advertisement   ☐ messaging

☐ blogging   ☐ networking

☐ cyberbullying   ☐ platform

☐ gaming   ☐ social marketing

☐ internet relay chat (IRC) ☐ social media

☐ media sharing   ☐ target audience

2. Starter activity

Describe three ways in which we might use a social network.

1. ....

2. ....

3. ....

3. Types of social media

List four different types of social media.

1. ....

2. ....

3. ....

4. ....

4. Features of social media

Draw a line from each feature to the matching description.

profile		users that are interested in reading all of your posts
friend requests		personal information about the user, their interests and hobbies
followers		based on your profiles, sponsored content is sent to you and placed on your page
targeted advertising		other users wanting to connect to your profile and content

5. Blogging

Describe the difference between a blog and a static website.

....

....

6. Advantages and disadvantages of social media

In the table below, tick whether the following are advantages or disadvantages of social media.

Statement	Advantages	Disadvantages
ability to chat with family and friends around the world		
many social networks are free to use		
fake news and biased opinion		
social interaction if living in a remote area		
cyberbullying		
lack of privacy and personal information being shared with other sites and advertisers		

7. Cyberbullying

Describe what is meant by the term 'cyberbullying'.

....

....

8. Plenary quick quiz

Question 1	Question 2	Question 3	Question 4	Question 5
What does IRC stand for?	What is a new message or image added to a page called?	True or false? Free social media sites are normally paid for by advertising.	True or false? More than half the world has a social media account.	Which of these commonly used items is a blog similar to?
☐ international reading course ☐ internet relay chat ☐ internet relay content ☐ internal relay communication	☐ post ☐ caption ☐ attachment ☐ event	☐ true ☐ false	☐ true ☐ false	☐ calendar ☐ newspaper ☐ to-do list ☐ diary

What makes a good spreadsheet?

1. Understand what makes a good spreadsheet.
2. Understand the layout and design tools that make a spreadsheet user-friendly.
3. Be able to add data from a simple survey to a spreadsheet.

1. 💬 Key word definitions

Tick the word or phrase when you know its meaning.

☐ data   ☐ user-friendly

☐ formatting   ☐ worksheet

☐ spreadsheet

☐ survey

2. Starter activity

Describe three things that can be done to make a spreadsheet user-friendly.

1. ....

2. ....

3. ....

3. Layout and design

List three layout and design tools that can be used to improve the look of a spreadsheet.

1. ....

2. ....

3. ....

4. Simple survey design

Look at the two questions below. Sketch a simple survey layout designed to collect answers from ten different people.

Question 1: What is your favourite type of computer game?

action
platform
racing

Question 2: How much would you spend on a new game?

5. Survey data

Please return to Unit 3 for a reminder of common spreadsheet formulas and functions. Using the spreadsheet template below, design how to enter your collected data from activity 4. It should include the following:

- titles
- responses from five people (These can be made up for this activity.)
- formulas to display
- how many have chosen either a, b or c
- average amount people would spend on a new game.

	A	B	C	D	E
1					
2					
3					
4					
5					

6. Locking a spreadsheet

Describe an example of where the creator of a spreadsheet might not want others to edit it.

....

....

7. Spreadsheet templates

When using a spreadsheet, describe the purpose of a template.

....

....

8. Plenary quick quiz

Question 1	Question 2	Question 3	Question 4	Question 5
Which tool is used to add clear edges to a table?	What type of data does a multiple choice question create?	True or false? Spreadsheets can only have one worksheet.	Which tool prevents other users from editing a spreadsheet?	A family budget, a loan calculator and invoices are all...?
☐ fill ☐ border ☐ font ☐ alignment	☐ qualitative ☐ quantitative	☐ true ☐ false	☐ insert sheet ☐ pivot table ☐ protect sheet ☐ print area	☐ templates ☐ worksheets ☐ page layouts ☐ house styles

Knowledge, data and information

◎ Learning objectives

1. Understand the terms 'knowledge', 'data', and 'information'.
2. Be able to describe examples of knowledge, data, and information.
3. Understand the terms 'primary' and 'secondary' data.
4. Be able to describe examples of primary and secondary data sources.

1. 💬 Key word definitions

Tick the word or phrase when you know its meaning.

☐ data	☐ qualitative data
☐ information	☐ quantitative data
☐ knowledge	☐ secondary data
☐ primary data	☐ survey

2. Starter activity

Draw a line from each feature to the matching description.

data		making use of new information
information		a value that, on its own, has no meaning
knowledge		data that has meaning

3. Knowledge, data and information

In the table below, tick whether the following examples could be classified as knowledge, data or information.

Statement	Knowledge	Data	Information
"This device isn't popular, let's change the design."			
1024			
Movie downloads = 120000			
99%			
"Based on this evidence, Python seems the best choice."			
Prices have increased by 20% this year.			

4. Your own examples of knowledge, data and information

Using the topic of social networking, create three statements that would fit into the categories of data, information and knowledge.

Data: ....

Information:...

Knowledge: ....

5. Primary and secondary data

Describe the difference between primary and secondary information.

....

....

6. Examples of primary and secondary data

In the table below, tick whether the examples could be classified as primary or secondary data.

Examples	Primary	Secondary
interviewing friends in your classroom		
downloading data from a statistics website		
going to the library to do research		
video recording a live event on your smartphone		

7. Primary and secondary data sources

Describe an example of a primary and secondary source, different from the ones in question 6.

Primary: ....

Secondary: ....

8. Plenary quick quiz

Question 1	Question 2	Question 3	Question 4	Question 5
True or false? Knowledge comes from valid data and relevant information.	Which of the following devices would be useful for collecting primary data?	True or false? Primary data is always more valid than secondary data.	Which of the following is a good source of secondary data?	True or false? Watching a recording of a live interview is still primary data.
☐ true ☐ false	☐ mouse ☐ speakers ☐ sound recorder ☐ router	☐ true ☐ false	☐ archive video ☐ chatting in person ☐ taking photos ☐ recording live audio	☐ true ☐ false

Sorting and filtering a spreadsheet

◎ Learning objectives

1. Understand the purpose of the sort function in a spreadsheet.
2. Understand the purpose of the filter function in a spreadsheet.
3. Demonstrate an ability to use the sort and filter functions to identify trends in a simple model.

1. 💬 Key word definitions

Tick the word or phrase when you know its meaning.

☐ alphabetically   ☐ descending   ☐ sort

☐ ascending   ☐ filter   ☐ trend

☐ criteria   ☐ numerically

☐ data   ☐ pattern

2. Starter activity

Describe the purpose of the sort function within a spreadsheet.

....

3. Using the sort and filter functions

Why is it important to carefully select the cells required when using the sort and filter functions?

....

4. Filter function

Describe the purpose of the filter function within a spreadsheet.

....

5. Example of a sort

In the table provided, show how the data would appear if an ascending sort was applied:

	A
1	Money spent
2	$32.00
3	$2.00
4	$12.00
5	$18.00
6	$45.00
7	$8.20
8	$8.50

	A
1	Money spent
2	
3	
4	
5	
6	
7	
8	

6. Example of a filter

In the table below, show how the data would appear if a filter was applied on only those with a size 6 shoe.

	A	B
1	Shoe size	Favourite style
2	7	Sneaker
3	6	Sneaker
4	6	Boot
5	5	Sandal
6	4	Sandal
7	6	Basketball
8	8	Slip-on

	A	B
1	Shoe size	Favourite style
2		
3		
4		
5		
6		
7		
8		

7. Trends in a simple model

Describe the meaning of the term 'trend' when analysing data.

....

....

....

....

8. Plenary quick quiz

Question 1	Question 2	Question 3	Question 4	Question 5
If the result of a sort was 3, 6, 8, which order has been used?	True or false? If a large table is sorted by one column, the other columns' contents will also reorder.	If the following numbers are sorted in descending order, what would be the result? 12, 65, 13, 11	What is the commonly used symbol used to represent a filter?	True or false? Filters cannot contain more than one criteria.
☐ descending ☐ ascending ☐ random ☐ ultimate	☐ true ☐ false	☐ 11, 12, 13, 65 ☐ 65, 12, 11, 13 ☐ 65, 13, 12, 11 ☐ 11, 13, 65, 12	☐ saucepan ☐ fork ☐ star ☐ funnel	☐ true ☐ false

Design techniques for an online advertisement

◎ Learning objectives

1. Understand the purpose of an online advertisement.
2. Be able to describe common sources of online advertisements.
3. Understand common layout and colour techniques for designing an online advertisement.

1. 💬 Key word definitions

Tick the word or phrase when you know its meaning.

- ☐ ad-blocker
- ☐ advertising
- ☐ attract
- ☐ complimentary colours
- ☐ design
- ☐ layout
- ☐ persuade
- ☐ social media platform
- ☐ target audience

2. Starter activity

Describe how online advertising is different from traditional printed advertising.

....

....

3. Online advertising

List three common features of an online advertisement.

1. ....

2. ....

3. ....

4. Locations of online advertising

Give three locations where a user is likely to see online advertisements.

1. ....

2. ....

3. ....

5. Layout techniques

Describe three things to consider when designing the layout of an online advertisement.

1. ....

2. ....

3. ....

6. Colour selection

The table below lists examples of things to consider when choosing colours for an online advertisement. Tick whether they are suitable or not suitable.

Examples	Suitable	Not suitable
stand out from the rest of the web page		
choose a small range of colours		
consider the colour theme of the product		
colours change every few seconds		

7. Ad-blockers

Describe the meaning of the term 'ad-blocker'

....

....

....

8. Plenary quick quiz

Question 1	Question 2	Question 3	Question 4	Question 5
What are online advertising sizes measured in?	True or false? Online advertisements cannot contain images.	How are the online adverts that users see selected?	Multiple adverts on a similar theme can be created using a…?	True or false? Ad-blockers can reduce the income of companies making the adverts.
☐ metres ☐ inches ☐ pixels ☐ millimetres	☐ true ☐ false	☐ based on search history ☐ based on user's location ☐ based on user's interests ☐ all of the above	☐ template ☐ layer ☐ spreadsheet ☐ mask	☐ true ☐ false

What makes a good chart?

◎ Learning objectives

1. Understand the purpose of a chart.
2. Describe examples of different chart types.
3. Understand how a pie chart can be used to display survey data.
4. Demonstrate how to select the most appropriate chart for a specific purpose.

1. 💬 Key word definitions

Tick the word or phrase when you know its meaning.

☐ bar chart	☐ line graph
☐ chart	☐ pie chart
☐ data	☐ scatter graph
☐ graph	☐ survey data

2. Starter activity

Describe the purpose of each of the following types of chart:

- Pie chart: ....
- Line graph: ....
- Bar/Column chart: ....
- Scatter graph: ....

3. Choosing an appropriate chart

The table below describes a range of scenarios. Tick the most appropriate chart type for each one.

Scenario	Pie chart	Line graph	Bar/Column chart	Scatter graph
battery charge time for different devices at different ages				
the proportion of users on different operating systems				
comparing the prices of similar smart watches				
the number of devices recycled over the last ten years				

4. Pie charts

Describe why a pie chart is ideal for displaying data collected during a survey.

....

....

....

5. Plenary quick quiz

Question 1	Question 2	Question 3	Question 4	Question 5
Which of the following is an interesting way to make a chart stand out?	What is often at the side of a pie chart?	What is another name used to describe the auto-tool for suggesting a graph?	Pie charts are most commonly used to display which data type?	True or false? Bar charts are normally presented horizontally and column charts vertically.
☐ 3D graphics ☐ more labels ☐ no labels ☐ 2D graphics	☐ lock ☐ animation ☐ key ☐ footer	☐ graphic design ☐ wizard ☐ window ☐ sprite	☐ currency ☐ dates ☐ decimals ☐ percentages	☐ true ☐ false

Designing an infographic

◎ Learning objectives

1. Understand the purpose of an infographic.
2. Understand the key elements that make up an infographic.
3. Demonstrate how to choose suitable infographic content for a given scenario.

1. 💬 Key word definitions

Tick the word or phrase when you know its meaning.

☐ chart   ☐ pictogram

☐ graph   ☐ timeline

☐ infographic   ☐ visuals

2. Starter activity

Describe what an infographic is.

....

....

....

3. Infographic tools

The table below describes a range of content that might be added to an infographic about smartphones. Tick the most appropriate way to present each piece of content.

Scenario	Text	Diagram	Timeline	Chart
the development of each generation of mobile phone				
the internal workings of a modern smartphone				
the impact of the smartphone on society				
users of smartphones over the last decade				

4. Creating an infographic.

Describe three ways of creating an infographic.

1. ....

2. ....

3. ....

5. Plenary quick quiz

Question 1	Question 2	Question 3	Question 4	Question 5
True or false? Infographics normally do not include photographs.	The page layout for an infographic is normally…?	Which of these applications would not usually be used to create an infographic?	True or false? There is no limit on how long an infographic can be.	What is combining simple graphics with a data chart to represent values known as?
☐ true ☐ false	☐ portrait ☐ landscape	☐ word processor ☐ presentation ☐ code editor ☐ online infographic creator	☐ true ☐ false	☐ an animation ☐ a special character ☐ a pictogram ☐ a GIF

Unit 4: Short answer questions

1. A typical 4-mark question

Working for a government information website, you are analysing data in a spreadsheet that will then be used in an infographic. A colleague has recommended using the sort and filter functions to help organise information for the reader.

Describe the purpose of the sort and filter tools in a spreadsheet. Provide an example of how each function could be used.

....

....

....

....

....

....

2. Another 4-mark question

As an online advertising designer, you are working on a sales promotion for a new fruit drink.

Describe two locations where this advertisement might appear. Give two tips for designing an effective advert for online use.

....

....

....

....

....

....

✏ Revision checklist

	MIND-MAP	MISSING WORDS	WRITE A QUIZ	FLASHCARDS	COVER AND WRITE
U4 L1 – Social media					
U4 L2 – What makes a good spreadsheet?					
U4 L3 – Knowledge, data and information					
U4 L4 – Sorting and filtering a spreadsheet					
U4 L5 & 6 – Design techniques for an online advertisement					
U4 L7 & 8 – What makes a good chart?					
U4 L9 & 10 – Designing an infographic					

Algorithms and turtle programming

◎ Learning objectives

1. Understand how an algorithm can be used to create 2D graphics.
2. Demonstrate how to create simple 2D shapes using the Python turtle program.

1. 💬 Key word definitions

Tick the word or phrase when you know its meaning.

☐ algorithm	☐ Python
☐ clear	☐ sequence
☐ commands	☐ turtle
☐ instructions	

2. Starter activity

Describe the meaning of the term 'algorithm'.

....

3. Turtle commands

Complete the gaps in the table below of common Python turtle commands.

Command	Description
name = turtle.Turtle()	used to name the drawing turtle, for example, marker
Import turtle	
fd(distance in pixels)	forward by a distance in pixels
bk(distance in pixels)	
rt(turn angle)	turn right by defined degrees
lt(turn angle)	
penup()	lift up the pen, so no line is drawn when moved
pendown()	
pensize(size in pixels)	sets the size of the drawing turtle
pencolor(colour)	

4. Examples of simple commands

Draw a line from the command to the matching description. The user has named the turtle 'floorPen' in these examples.

floorPen = turtle.Turtle()		reverses the pen 90 units
floorPen.pencolour("red")		turns the pen 90 degrees to the right
floorPen.bk(90)		sets the pen colour to red
floorPen.rt(90)		creates a new turtle called 'floorPen'

5. Creating simple shapes in Python

Look at the example Python program below. Draw the shape it creates in the box provided.

```
#Simple Shape 1
import turtle
floorPen = turtle.Turtle()
floorPen.pencolor("Black")
floorPen.fd(200)
floorPen.rt(90)
floorPen.fd(100)
floorPen.rt(90)
floorPen.fd(200)
floorPen.rt(90)
floorPen.fd(100)
```

6. Programming a simple shape

Complete the Python program below to create the simple shape shown.

```
#Simple Shape 2
import turtle
floorPen = turtle.Turtle()
```

....

....

....

....

....

....

7. Plenary quick quiz

Question 1	Question 2	Question 3	Question 4	Question 5
Where does the turtle in Python always start?	Which command will turn the turtle from straight up to straight down?	Which of the following will select a blue pen?	True or false? Forward can be used instead of fd.	True or false? It is good practice to name the turtle pen.
☐ top left	☐ rt(180)	☐ pencolor(blue)	☐ true	☐ true
☐ bottom left	☐ rt(90)	☐ pencolour("blue")	☐ false	☐ false
☐ centre	☐ lt(90)	☐ pencolor=blue		
☐ top centre	☐ bk(180)	☐ pencolor("blue")		

Sequencing and iteration algorithms

◎ Learning objectives

1. Understand the terms 'sequencing' and 'iteration'.
2. Understand how sequencing and iteration can be used in Python.
3. Demonstrate the use of sequencing and iteration in a Python turtle program.

1. 💬 Key word definitions

Tick the word or phrase when you know its meaning.

- ☐ algorithm
- ☐ code
- ☐ counted loop
- ☐ efficiency
- ☐ iteration
- ☐ loop
- ☐ RAM (random access memory)
- ☐ repeat/repetition
- ☐ sequence

2. Starter activity

Describe the meaning of the following terms:

- Sequencing: ....

....

- Iteration: ....

....

3. A sequencing example

Write a simple Python code that will create the following output:

....

....

....

This is a smile :)

This means sad :(

This is a big smile :D

4. An iteration example

Write a simple Python code that will create the following output:

....

....

....

....

....

....

....

....

V

E

R

T

I

C

A

L

5. Using iteration in Python

Complete the missing three lines from the Python program below that creates a simple red square with sides of length 75 pixels.

```
#Iteration 1
import turtle
marker = turtle.Turtle()
marker.pencolour("red")
for line in range (4):
    marker.fd(75)
    marker.lt(90)
```

6. Creating a shape using iteration

Follow the example Python program below and draw the shape that it creates in the box provided.

```
#Iteration 2
import turtle
maker = turtle.Turtle()
marker.pencolour("yellow")
for line in range (3):
    marker.fd(100)
    marker.lt(120)
```

7. Plenary quick quiz

Question 1	Question 2	Question 3	Question 4	Question 5
Repeating an action until a condition is met is called…?	Following one simple step after another is called…?	What should follow a line using the 'for' command?	How many iterations might be used to create a hexagon?	Making an algorithm more efficient will…?
☐ sequencing ☐ selection ☐ iteration ☐ drawing	☐ sequencing ☐ selection ☐ iteration ☐ drawing	☐ an empty line ☐ a semi colon ☐ inverted commas ☐ an indentation	☐ 6 ☐ 7 ☐ 8 ☐ 9	☐ increase the number of lines ☐ reduce the number of lines ☐ have no impact ☐ rename variables

Programming errors

◎ Learning objectives

1. Understand the importance of error checking in a program.
2. Understand the terms 'logic error' and 'syntax error'.
3. Demonstrate an ability to spot and resolve logic and syntax errors in a simple Python program.

1. 💬 Key word definitions

Tick the word or phrase when you know its meaning.

☐ bug   ☐ logic error

☐ computer program   ☐ sequence

☐ debugging   ☐ syntax error

☐ error

2. Starter activity

Explain why error checking is important when programming.

....

....

....

3. Logic and syntax errors

Describe the meaning of the following types of error:

- Logic error: ....

....

- Syntax error: ....

....

4. Basic error checking

Describe three simple checks that can be carried out before running any program.

1. ....

....

2. ....

....

3. ....

....

5. Examples of logic and syntax errors

There are two logic errors and two syntax errors in the program below. The first image shows the result of errors and the second shows how it should look.

```
#Octagon

import turtle

marker = turtle.Turtle()

markker.pencolor(green)

for line in range(9):
    marker.fd(100)
    marker.lt(54)
```

code with errors   code without errors

State the errors that have been made.

Logic error 1:	
Logic error 2:	
Syntax error 1:	
Syntax error 2:	

6. Plenary quick quiz

Question 1	Question 2	Question 3	Question 4	Question 5
Which of the following is not a syntax error?	True or false? Logic errors should be spotted as a program is designed.	What type of error will be caused by failing to add an indentation where it is required?	True or false? A common syntax error is the spelling of color.	What is another term used for error checking?
☐ incorrectly spelled input function ☐ missing closing bracket ☐ incorrect angle within a graphic ☐ missing colon following an IF command	☐ true ☐ false	☐ logic error ☐ syntax error	☐ true ☐ false	☐ debunking ☐ debugging ☐ declutter ☐ debating

Using lists in a Python program

◎ Learning objectives

1. Understand the purpose of using lists in a Python program.
2. Understand how to create and edit lists.
3. Demonstrate the use of lists in a simple Python program.

1. 💬 Key word definitions

Tick the word or phrase when you know its meaning.

☐ index

☐ interactivity

☐ list

☐ pseudorandom

☐ random

☐ response

☐ user generated

2. Starter activity

Describe the meaning of a list in Python programming.

....

....

3. Lists in Python

Give two properties of lists used in Python.

1. ....

....

2. ....

....

4. Creating lists in Python

Create a Python list for each data type.

- String list of names: Joanna, Amos, Fletcher, Raya

....

....

- Integer list of values: 161, 47, 13, 15

....

....

- String list of floats: 7.34, 4.65, 12.45, 2.1

....

....

5. Editing lists

Consider the list below. Add the lines of code that would be needed to carry out the two actions.

highScore = [201, 182, 191, 222]

i.   Delete the number 182.

....

....

ii. Add the number 250 to the end of the list.

....

....

6. A random choice

A program requires a random day of the week to be displayed.

On your computer or table, create a Python list called 'days'. It should contain all seven days and use the random function. Print a random day from it.

7. Pseudorandom

Describe the meaning of the term 'pseudorandom'.

....

....

....

8. Plenary quick quiz

Question 1	Question 2	Question 3	Question 4	Question 5
When creating a list with strings, which symbol should come before and after each item?	What is the index of the first value in a list?	What will the following action do? del name[1]	A program using the random function requires which line at the start?	True or false? Pseudorandom is not truly random.
☐ inverted commas ☐ colons ☐ question marks ☐ dollar signs	☐ 3 ☐ 2 ☐ 1 ☐ 0	☐ delete the first item in a list ☐ delete the second item in a list ☐ print once ☐ delete the last item in a list	☐ insert random ☐ random import ☐ import random ☐ import.random	☐ true ☐ false

Use of selection in an algorithm

◎ Learning objectives

1. Understand the purpose of selection in an algorithm.
2. Understand how selection can be used in a visual or text-based language.
3. Demonstrate an ability to apply selection to a simple brief.

1. 💬 Key word definitions

Tick the word or phrase when you know its meaning.

☐ algorithm

☐ input

☐ selection

2. Starter activity

Describe the purpose of using selection within an algorithm.

....

....

....

3. Selection responses

List three types of response that could be used within a selection algorithm.

1. ....

2. ....

3. ....

4. A simple selection flowchart

In the box provided, draw a simple visual flowchart that follows the algorithm below.

- Start
- Enter smartphone PIN
- Check if PIN is correct
- If correct, open smartphone
- If incorrect, ask for PIN again
- Stop when smartphone is open.

5. Selection algorithms in Python

Describe the purpose of the following two Python functions.

- IF ....

....

- ELSE ....

....

6. Comparison operators

Draw a line from the comparison operators to the matching description.

		greater than or equal to
>		less than or equal to
<		less than
>=		greater than
<=		

7. Creating a selection program

Create a selection program using Python that meets the following brief:

An online shoe shop only has shoes in stock that are sizes 9 and below. When asked about their size, if the user replies 9 or under, they are welcomed to the shop. If the response is higher than 9, they are asked to try again later.

....

....

....

....

....

8. Plenary quick quiz

Question 1	Question 2	Question 3	Question 4	Question 5
Which flowchart function is represented by a rectangle?	Which shape is used in a flowchart to represent a question?	How many outputs does a flowchart decision have?	Which symbol must appear at the end of an IF function?	When using pseudocode, which term is also used in a selection algorithm?
☐ input or output	☐ square	☐ 1	☐ inverted commas	☐ THEN
☐ decision	☐ rectangle	☐ 2	☐ colon	☐ THEREFORE
☐ start	☐ diamond	☐ 3	☐ question mark	☐ THAT
☐ stop	☐ circle	☐ 4	☐ dollar sign	☐ THUS

Creating a simple chatbot

◎ Learning objectives

1. Understand the concept of a chatbot.
2. Understand the key components of a simple chatbot program.
3. Demonstrate an ability to create a simple chatbot using Python.

1. 💬 Key word definitions

Tick the word or phrase when you know its meaning.

- ☐ AI (artificial intelligence)
- ☐ chatbot
- ☐ function
- ☐ program
- ☐ question
- ☐ response
- ☐ Turing Test

2. Starter activity

Describe the purpose of a chatbot.

....

....

....

3. A simple chatbot program

Consider the example chatbot program below. In the table, add the number referring to the correct annotation. Number 1 has been done for you.

```
#Chatbot
import random
import time                                                          ← 1

chatDrink = ["chocolate", "strawberry", "vanilla", "raspberry"]
print("Welcome to Chatbot")                                          2
name = input("What is your name?")  ←
print("Hi there",name,"it's great to meet you!")
place = input("What is your favourite milkshake flavour?")           3
time.sleep(2)  ←
print("That sounds amazing. I love", random.choice(chatDrink)) ←
day =  input("Have you had a good day?")                             4
day = day.lower()  ←
                                                                     5
if day =="yes":
        print("Good to hear that, me too.")
else:
        print("I know tomorrow will be better.")  ←
print("Really enjoyed the chat, speak soon.")                        6
```

Number	Annotation
1	import random and time functions
	the user's response is converted to lowercase
	this message is given when there is a response other than yes
	a delay is used to make it seem like the chatbot is thinking
	a random drink is chosen from the chatDrink list
	user's name is saved as variable name

4.   Communicating with a chatbot

Describe two ways we can communicate with a chatbot.

1. ....

2. ....

5. Key components of a chatbot

List three components that all chatbots should follow.

1. ....

2. ....

3. ....

6. Turing test

Describe the purpose of the Turing test.

....

....

7. Plenary quick quiz

Question 1	Question 2	Question 3	Question 4	Question 5
In which decade did Alan Turin devise the Turin test?	Out of the following, where wouldn't we normally find a chatbot?	What does AI stand for?	What function is used to give the appearance of thinking?	What does the operator == represent?
☐ 1940s ☐ 1950s ☐ 1960s ☐ 1970s	☐ restaurant ☐ online store ☐ computer support site ☐ online games	☐ artificial information ☐ android interface ☐ artificial intelligence	☐ random.choice ☐ print() ☐ input() ☐ time.sleep()	☐ greater than ☐ exactly equal to ☐ less than ☐ almost

Subprograms in an algorithm

◎ Learning objectives

1. Understand the purpose of a subprogram.
2. Understand how a subprogram can be used in real-life situations.
3. Demonstrate use of a subprogram in a range of scenarios.

1. 💬 Key word definitions

Tick the word or phrase when you know its meaning.

☐ algorithm	☐ program
☐ code	☐ return
☐ function	☐ subprogram
☐ procedure	☐ subroutine

2. Starter activity

Describe the purpose of a subprogram.

....

....

....

3. Subprogram characteristics

List three characteristics of a subprogram.

1. ....

2. ....

3. ....

4. Examples of where subprograms are used

Describe three real life examples of where subprograms are used.

1. ....

2. ....

3. ....

5. Procedures and functions

In the table below, tick whether the subprograms described are procedures or functions.

Subprogram description	Procedures	Functions
reset a stopwatch variable to zero		
add the current date to a document		
open a PIN entry screen		
display a user warning message		

6. Creating a subprogram in Python

Using Python, create a simple subprogram that chooses a random number between 0 and 9 inclusive.

....

....

7. Adding a subprogram

The program below requires a random number subprogram to help create a four-digit PIN number. Using the subprogram from question 6, annotate where the following two elements need to be placed:

- the defined subprogram
- the program being called into use.

```
#four digit PIN
import random

print ("This program will generate you a new for digit PIN")
print ("Your new PIN number is:")
digit1 =
digit2 =
digit3 =
digit4 =
print
```

8. Plenary quick quiz

Question 1	Question 2	Question 3	Question 4	Question 5
True or false? A subprogram can only be used once in a program.	What is another name for a subprogram?	How does each subprogram need to be defined?	True or false? A procedure always returns a value to the main program.	In Python, what is another name for a subprogram?
☐ true ☐ false	☐ subsystem ☐ subfunction ☐ subroutine ☐ subnetwork	☐ def *name*(): ☐ sub.*name* ☐ define=*name* ☐ def (*name*)	☐ true ☐ false	☐ routine ☐ action ☐ function ☐ module

Creating a missing word game

◎ Learning objectives

1. Understand how multiple programming techniques can be combined to create a complex program.
2. Demonstrate an ability to create a simple missing word game in Python.

1. 💬 Key word definitions

Tick the word or phrase when you know its meaning.

☐ algorithm   ☐ string

☐ coding   ☐ user

☐ input

2. Starter activity

List five programming techniques you have studied so far that could be incorporated into a larger program.

1. ....

2. ....

3. ....

4. ....

5. ....

3. The capital city game brief

In this section, your challenge is to create a similar program to the Python missing word game shown in the Student book. The following brief describes the purpose of the game:

The game presents the user with three countries and for each, they have to name the capital city. Three possible cities are provided and the user selects one. They are then told if they have got the answer right or wrong.

Program break down

The program can be broken down into the following key elements:

- three questions asking the user to name capital cities
- each question requires an answer
- the answers can be stored in a list
- the user selects an answer from the list
- the user is told if they have selected the correct city.

Tips

Your program should include all of the following techniques. When you have included each one, tick them off the list.

Technique	Tick
Plan out your program before writing any code.	
Create a Python list of three cities.	
Create a subprogram for the questions.	
Create three questions, one country for each city.	
Insert the subprogram where appropriate.	

Your program

Unit 5: Short answer questions

1. A typical 4-mark question

You are working with a group of young children, experimenting with coding a floor turtle that draws shapes on the floor.

You are demonstrating how to program the same shape using sequencing and iteration.

Describe the difference between sequencing and iteration, and explain how iteration can be used to create a triangle.

....

....

....

....

....

....

2. Another 4-mark question

You are working on a contact address book for a smartphone application and you are experimenting with lists to store names and numbers.

Describe the purpose of Python lists and share one fact about them. Give two examples of Python lists, one containing names and one containing numbers.

....

....

....

....

....

....

✏ Revision checklist

	MIND-MAP	MISSING WORDS	WRITE A QUIZ	FLASHCARDS	COVER AND WRITE
U5 L1 & 2– Algorithms and turtle programming					
U5 L3 & 4 – Sequencing and iteration algorithms					
U5 L5 – Programming errors					
U5 L6 – Using lists in a Python program					
U5 L7 – Use of selection in an algorithm					
U5 L8 – Creating a simple chatbot					
U5 L9 – Subprograms in an algorithm					
U5 L10 – Creating a missing word game					

Surveillance technology

◎ Learning objectives

1. Understand surveillance technology in the context of computing.
2. Understand how technology is being used to create surveillance and security tools.
3. Understand a range of scenarios where surveillance equipment might be used.

1. 💬 Key word definitions

Tick the word or phrase when you know its meaning.

☐ facial recognition   ☐ security

☐ hack   ☐ spyware

☐ hardware   ☐ surveillance

☐ intercept

2. Starter activity

In the table below, describe an example of computer surveillance that could use the technology listed.

Technology	Example of surveillance
Smartphone	
USB stick	
Digital cameras	
GPS equipment	

3. Social media surveillance

Describe how social media activity can be used as a surveillance tool.

....

....

....

4. Workplace surveillance

List three examples of how employers might observe work carried out by employees at home.

1. ....

....

2. ....

....

3. ....

....

5. Surveillance scenarios

In the table below, give an example of computer surveillance that might be carried out for each scenario.

Scenario	Potential surveillance
tracking a person across a city or town	
intercepting messages	
looking at someone's computer files	

6. Spyware

Describe what is meant by the term 'spyware'.

7. Plenary quick quiz

Question 1	Question 2	Question 3	Question 4	Question 5
What technology does facial recognition use?	What does GPS stand for?	Which of the following is a term used to describe reading a message between two people without their knowledge?	True or false? The police can access anyone's search history via their internet service provider.	What should you do if a new smartphone game asks to access your location?
☐ microphones ☐ speakers ☐ digital cameras ☐ keyboard	☐ global positioning system ☐ globe position sentry ☐ global picture system ☐ geo position secure	☐ intelligence ☐ intercept ☐ inform ☐ interstellar	☐ true ☐ false	☐ accept it ☐ deny access ☐ delete the game ☐ find out why the game might need access to your location

Types of software

Learning objectives

1. Understand the terms application, operating and utility software.
2. Describe examples of each type of software.
3. Demonstrate an ability to choose the most appropriate software type for a given scenario.
4. Understand how the same software types apply to all computer based devices.

1. Key word definitions

Tick the word or phrase when you know its meaning.

☐ application software   ☐ open source
☐ computer-aided design   ☐ operating system
☐ desktop publishing   ☐ presentation software
☐ graphics software   ☐ sound editing
☐ image editing   ☐ utility software
☐ office applications

2. Starter activity

Draw a line from the type of software to the matching description.

application		the link between hardware and software
operating system		software that supports the operating system
utility		programs we use on a day-to-day basis

3. Examples of software

In the table below, suggest common examples of each type of software.

Application	Operating system	Utility

4. Office software

List four common packages that are normally part of an Office-based suite of programs.

1. ....

2. ....

3. ....

4. ....

5. Software choices

Tick the most appropriate software for each of the scenarios in the table below.

Scenario	Application	Operating system	Utility
A virus needs to be removed from a computer.			
A new computer has been purposed and has no software installed.			
A spreadsheet needs to be created for a new business.			

6. Devices that require computer software

Other than a desktop or laptop computer, describe three devices that require computer software.

1. ....

2. ....

3. ....

7. Open source

Describe the meaning of the term 'open source'.

....

....

....

8. Plenary quick quiz

Question 1	Question 2	Question 3	Question 4	Question 5
Which type of software is required before the other two can be installed?	True or false? The Apple operating system was developed before the Windows system.	True or false? When building your own computer, you will need to install an operating system.	Protecting files using encryption would require which type of software?	True or false? It is okay to edit the programming of open source software.
☐ application ☐ operating system ☐ utility	☐ true ☐ false	☐ true ☐ false	☐ application ☐ operating system ☐ utility	☐ true ☐ false

Operating systems

Learning objectives

1. Understand the purpose of an operating system.
2. Understand the key roles of an operating system as part of a whole system.
3. Understand the different types of operating system.

1. Key word definitions

Tick the word or phrase when you know its meaning.

- ☐ command line interface (CLI)
- ☐ dialogue
- ☐ gesture/touch
- ☐ graphical user interface (GUI)
- ☐ memory management
- ☐ multi-tasking
- ☐ operating system
- ☐ peripherals
- ☐ security
- ☐ user interface

2. Starter activity

Describe three key processes that could not happen without an operating system.

1. ....

2. ....

3. ....

3. Operating system roles

Draw a line from the operating system roles to the matching description.

user interface		on-screen display that allows the user to interact with the computer, move the mouse and see applications
memory management		allows two or more applications to run at the same time
peripherals		monitoring and controlling access to programs and data and preventing any unauthorised access
multi-tasking		allocating memory space to programs and data
security		allows applications to interact with devices connected to the computer

4. Devices with operating systems

List three devices that use an operating system, other than desktop and laptop computers.

1. ....

2. ....

3. ....

5. Difference between GUI and CLI

Describe the difference between a GUI (graphical user interface) and a CLI (command line interface).

....

....

....

6. Interacting with an operating system

In the table below, tick the most appropriate way to interact with an operating system for each task.

Task	GUI (graphical user interface)	CLI (command line interface)	Dialogue	Gesture/ touch
clicking and dragging files and folders				
asking a smart speaker for a radio station				
swiping through digital photos				
programming an old computer from the 1970s				

7. Plenary quick quiz

Question 1	Question 2	Question 3	Question 4	Question 5
Playing a game and checking emails are an example of...?	Which of the following is not a peripheral device?	Which of the following now commonly uses dialogue control as its main interface?	True or false? Early operating systems used a CLI.	What is pinch to zoom an example of?
☐ multi-tasking ☐ model-tasking ☐ multi-programming ☐ multiple tests	☐ printer ☐ mouse ☐ graphics card ☐ keyboard	☐ games console ☐ smart TV ☐ smart speaker ☐ tablet	☐ true ☐ false	☐ GUI ☐ CLI ☐ dialogue ☐ gesture/touch

Utility software

Learning objectives

1. Understand the purpose of utility software.
2. Understand the different types of utility software.
3. Demonstrate an ability to choose the most appropriate utility software for a given scenario.

1. Key word definitions

Tick the word or phrase when you know its meaning.

☐ anti-malware   ☐ defragmentation
☐ anti-spyware   ☐ disk organisation
☐ antivirus   ☐ file transfer
☐ back-up   ☐ firewall
☐ compression   ☐ maintenance

2. Starter activity

Describe the purpose of utility software.

....

....

....

3. Utility software categories

Draw a line from the utility software category to the matching description.

security		ensures files are organised and disks are correctly formatted
disk organisation		keeping an eye on system updates, running back-ups
maintenance		preventing unauthorised access to your computer

4. System information

List two examples of the information that might be displayed by utility software designed to analyse system information.

1. ....

2. ....

5. Types of utility software

In the table below, tick the most appropriate category for each of the examples described.

Software	Security	Disk organisation	Maintenance
anti-virus			
disk defragmentation			
back-up			
firewall			
system clean-up			
compression			
encryption			
disk formatting			
system information			

6. Updating utility software

Why is it important that utility software is kept up to date?

....

....

....

7. Plenary quick quiz

Question 1	Question 2	Question 3	Question 4	Question 5
True or false? A computer worm can copy itself to other computers.	What is software designed by a separate company known as?	Accessing files using a secret key is part of which process?	True or false? If software is not updated, it can become a security risk.	Which of the following tools is designed to block unwanted network access to a computer?
☐ true ☐ false	☐ first party ☐ second party ☐ third party ☐ fourth party	☐ defragmentation ☐ compression ☐ backing up ☐ encryption	☐ true ☐ false	☐ compression ☐ firewall ☐ anti-malware ☐ disk format

Internet hardware

◎ Learning objectives

1. Understand the hardware required to connect to the internet.
2. Understand the role of some of the key hardware devices.
3. Demonstrate an ability to choose the required hardware for a given scenario.

1. 💬 Key word definitions

Tick the word or phrase when you know its meaning.

- ☐ data packet
- ☐ devices
- ☐ home network
- ☐ internet protocol address (IP)
- ☐ internet service provider (ISP)
- ☐ internet
- ☐ modem
- ☐ network interface card (NIC)
- ☐ switch
- ☐ wireless access point (WAP)

2. Starter activity

Describe two wired and two wireless devices that might be connected to a home network.

Wired 1: ....

Wired 2: ....

Wireless 1: ....

Wireless 2: ....

3. Internet hardware

In the table below, tick the hardware that matches the description.

Hardware	Switch	Wireless access point (WAP)	Network interface card (NIC)	Modem
provides a connection for wireless devices to the local network				
connects directly to the router and directs data to and from specific devices				
allows a computer or laptop to connect to a wired or wireless network				
converts the data from the internet into a form your network can understand and vice-versa				

4. Combining internet hardware

Which two devices listed in question 3 are commonly combined in home internet connections?

....

....

5. Data packets

Draw a line from the data packet component to the matching description.

packet header		part of the actual message data
packet body		this signals the end of the data packet and checks the packet is complete
packet footer		information about where the data is from, where it is going and its position in the message

6. Connection scenarios

Consider the two scenarios below and write a description of the route that will be taken from the internet to the user.

Scenario	Description of route
sending a presentation from a tablet to a laptop	
ordering takeaway pizza using a smart speaker	

7. Plenary quick quiz

Question 1	Question 2	Question 3	Question 4	Question 5
True or false? NICs (Network interface cards) can only be wired.	A common feature of a smart device is being able to…?	What does the S in ISP stand for?	True or false? Sending an email from one device to another in the same house will still access the internet.	What part of a data packet are source and destination a part of?
☐ true ☐ false	☐ access the internet ☐ speak ☐ play games ☐ recommend music	☐ system ☐ security ☐ service ☐ solution	☐ true ☐ false	☐ header ☐ body ☐ footer

Wireless communication technology

◎ Learning objectives

1. Understand the purpose of wireless communication technology.
2. Understand the purpose of near-field communication (NFC), Wi-Fi and Bluetooth.
3. Describe some of the advantages and disadvantages of each technology.
4. Demonstrate an ability to choose the most appropriate technology for a given scenario.

1. 💬 Key word definitions

Tick the word or phrase when you know its meaning.

- ☐ Bluetooth
- ☐ connectivity
- ☐ near-field communication (NFC)
- ☐ Wi-Fi
- ☐ wireless

2. Starter activity

Describe what is meant by the term 'wireless communication technology'.

....

....

....

3. Wi-Fi technology

List two uses of Wi-Fi technology.

1. ....

2. ....

4. Near-field communication (NFC)

List two uses of near-field communication (NFC).

1. ....

2. ....

5. Bluetooth technology

List two uses of Bluetooth technology.

1. ....

2. ....

6. Advantages and disadvantages of wireless communication technology

Describe two advantages and disadvantages for each wireless technology.

	Advantages	Disadvantages
Wi-Fi	1. .... 2.	1. .... 2. ....
NFC	1. .... 2.	1. .... 2. ....
Bluetooth	1. .... 2.	1. .... 2. ....

7. Connection scenarios

Tick the most appropriate wireless technology for the three scenarios below.

Scenario	Wi-Fi	NFC	Bluetooth
paying for a hot chocolate in a café			
connecting a tablet to a home network			
connecting to a new pair of wireless headphones			

8. Plenary quick quiz

Question 1	Question 2	Question 3	Question 4	Question 5
Which wireless technology has a range of only a few centimetres?	Which of the following does not normally use Bluetooth?	Which of the following will provide the fastest connection?	Which technology is ideal for swapping contacts between two smartphones?	True or false? Leaving a Bluetooth connection open can be a security risk.
☐ Wi-Fi ☐ NFC ☐ Bluetooth ☐ mobile data	☐ keyboard ☐ mouse ☐ monitor ☐ headphones	☐ Wi-Fi ☐ NFC ☐ Bluetooth ☐ ethernet	☐ Wi-Fi ☐ NFC ☐ Bluetooth ☐ ethernet	☐ true ☐ false

The internet and the world wide web

◎ Learning objectives

1. Understand the difference between the internet and the world wide web.
2. Understand the process of requesting access to and connecting to a website.
3. Understand the key hardware and software components that make the internet possible.

1. 💬 Key word definitions

Tick the word or phrase when you know its meaning.

☐ data packet

☐ domain name system (DNS)

☐ hosting

☐ HyperText mark-up language (HTML)

☐ internet service provider (ISP)

☐ internet

☐ IP address

☐ internet service provider (ISP)

☐ uniform resource locator (URL)

☐ web browser

☐ web server

☐ world wide web (WWW)

2. Starter activity

Describe the difference between the internet and the world wide web.

....

....

3. HTML

Describe the purpose of the HTML programming language.

....

4. Connecting to a website

These statements make up the sequence of events after typing a web address into a browser. They are in the wrong order. Write a number in the box next to each statement to show the right order.

	web browser opens website located at IP address
	web address typed in
	DNS server sends IP address to browser
	DNS server searches for an IP address that matches the web address
	web browser asks DNS server about web address
	web browser accesses the internet via modem, router and ISP

5. Website addresses

Describe the need for website addresses when browsing the internet.

....

....

6. Essential components

The following descriptions are of essential internet components. Tick the correct description to match the component.

Description	IP address	Internet service provider (ISP)	Domain name system (DNS) server	Web server
An international naming service that links internet addresses with an IP address.				
A network connected computer server that stores website files.				
A company that provides access to the internet to homes, schools and workplaces.				
An identifying address assigned to every network connected device.				

7. Hosting files

Describe the meaning of the term 'hosting' when discussing the internet.

....

....

....

....

8. Plenary quick quiz

Question 1	Question 2	Question 3	Question 4	Question 5
What does HTML stand for?	Every device on a network is assigned a unique...?	True or false? There are only six DNS servers across the world.	What does DNS stand for?	HTML files are designed to be displayed by a...?
☐ hypertext mark-up language ☐ hyper transfer module language ☐ hidden text mark-up logic	☐ DNS ☐ IP address ☐ ISP ☐ CAD	☐ true ☐ false	☐ digital name server ☐ domain network search ☐ defined name system ☐ domain name system	☐ word processor ☐ image editor ☐ web browser ☐ notepad

Surveillance ethics

◎ Learning objectives

1. Understand the reasons given for increased surveillance and the tracking of individuals.
2. Understand some of the moral and ethical questions being raised on this topic.
3. Understand some of the arguments for and against surveillance technology.
4. Demonstrate an understanding of the importance of researching controversial topics.

1. 💬 Key word definitions

Tick the word or phrase when you know its meaning.

- ☐ closed-circuit television (CCTV)
- ☐ eavesdrop
- ☐ ethics
- ☐ geolocation information
- ☐ ID cards
- ☐ legal
- ☐ moral
- ☐ research

2. Starter activity

List three reasons governments give for the increased use of surveillance technology.

1. ....
2. ....
3. ....

3. Commercial surveillance

List three reasons commercial organisations give for the increased use of surveillance technology.

1. ....
2. ....
3. ....

4. Solving crimes

List three examples of how technology might be used to solve a crime.

1. ....
2. ....
3. ....

5. Moral and ethical questions

List three moral or ethical questions that have been raised in the use of surveillance technology.

1. ....

2. ....

3. ....

6. For and against increased surveillance

In the table below, tick whether each statement is either for or against increased surveillance technology.

Statement	For	Against
increased security and data protection		
more secure online shopping and banking		
lack of freedom		
people may be incorrectly charged with a crime		
governments must keep up with criminals		
concerns about data sharing		
being able to stop criminal activity and cyberattacks		
information being used without our permission		

7. Plenary quick quiz

Question 1	Question 2	Question 3	Question 4	Question 5
Which of the following is not a reason given for more surveillance?	Which of the following is often shared online?	True or false? Criminals are often found to be using technology more advanced than law enforcement agencies.	Facial recognition and thumb print recognition are now commonly used in which type of device?	True or false? Facial recognition and intercepting messages have resulted in crimes being prevented.
☐ increased safety ☐ cheaper products ☐ confirming identity ☐ better social media	☐ search history ☐ hobbies and interests ☐ bank statements ☐ medical history	☐ true ☐ false	☐ smart speaker ☐ smart TV ☐ smartphone ☐ credit cards	☐ true ☐ false

Data breaches and cyber-crime

◉ Learning objectives

1. Understand the terms data breach and cyber-attack.
2. Understand the effects of data being stolen.
3. Understand the technical weaknesses that leave a computer vulnerable.
4. Understand some of the prevention strategies that can be used.

1. 💬 Key word definitions

Tick the word or phrase when you know its meaning.

☐ cyber-attack

☐ data breach

☐ phishing

☐ portable storage device

☐ unpatched software

2. Starter activity

Describe the meaning of the term 'data breach'.

....

....

....

3. Data breach

List three examples of the types of data that might be stolen in a data breach.

1. ....

2. ....

3. ....

4. Cyber-attack

List three examples of a cyber-attack.

1. ....

2. ....

3. ....

5. Phishing scams

Describe how a phishing scam tries to steal data.

....

....

....

6. Personal data

For each example of personal data being stolen, describe the possible consequences.

Information stolen	Possible consequences
username and password	
personal details, including date of birth	
credit card details	

7. Preventative strategies

For each of the weaknesses below, describe a potential way they could be prevented.

Weakness	Prevention
poor password protection	
use of portable storage devices	
unpatched, or poorly updated, software	
messages that can be intercepted and read	

8. Plenary quick quiz

Question 1	Question 2	Question 3	Question 4	Question 5
True or false? Personal details are often taken from social networks.	Which of the following is a strong password?	Which of the following are often used to contain spyware?	Secretly listening to someone's conversation is called…?	When receiving a phishing email, what should you do?
☐ true ☐ false	☐ Password1 ☐ Ijef453&EF2 ☐ 12345 ☐ secret	☐ monitor ☐ printers ☐ mouse ☐ USB stick	☐ hacking ☐ phishing ☐ eavesdropping ☐ patching	☐ delete it ☐ reply to it ☐ click the link ☐ forward it to others

Unit 6: Short answer questions

1. A typical 4-mark question

As a surveillance technology expert, you are giving a talk to new employees about examples of surveillance technology.

Describe two examples of surveillance technology and their uses.

....

....

....

....

....

....

2. Another 4-mark question

As a smartwatch designer, you are looking at including near-field communication technology (NFC) into the product.

Describe what NFC is and how a smartwatch might make use of it.

....

....

....

....

....

....

✏ Revision checklist

	MIND-MAP	MISSING WORDS	WRITE A QUIZ	FLASHCARDS	COVER AND WRITE
U6 L1 – Surveillance technology					
U6 L2 – Types of software					
U6 L3 – Operating systems					
U6 L4 – Utility software					
U6 L5 – Internet hardware					
U6 L6 – Wireless communication technology					
U6 L7 – The internet and the world wide web					
U6 L8 & 9 – Surveillance ethics					
U6 L10 – Data breaches and cyber-crime					

Published by Pearson Education Limited, 80 Strand, London, WC2R 0RL.
www.pearson.com/international-schools

Copies of official specifications for all Pearson Edexcel qualifications may be found on the website:
https://qualifications.pearson.com

Text © Pearson Education Limited 2022
Project managed and edited by Just Content
Designed and typeset by PDQ Digital Media Solutions Ltd
Picture research by Integra
Original illustrations © Pearson Education Limited 2022
Cover design © Pearson Education Limited 2022
Cover illustration © Beehive/Andrew Pagram

The right of Paul Clowrey to be identified as the author of this work has been asserted by him in
accordance with the Copyright, Designs and Patents Act 1988.

First published 2022

24
10 9 8 7 6 5 4

British Library Cataloguing in Publication Data
A catalogue record for this book is available from the British Library

ISBN 978 1 292 40437 0

Printed in Great Britain by Bell and Bain Ltd, Glasgow

Acknowledgements

The author and publisher would like to thank the following individuals and organisations for permission to reproduce
photographs, illustrations, and text:
KEY (t – top, c – center, b – bottom, tl – top left, tr – top right)

Page 30; Screenshot from Scratch program, https://scratch.mit.edu

All other images © Pearson Education